10/20

Please return/renew this item by the
last date shown to avoid a charge.
Books may also be renewed by phone
and Internet. May not be renewed if
required by another reader.
www.libraries.barnet.gov.uk

BARNET
LONDON BOROUGH

While the events described and some of the characters in these twelve stories may be based on actual historical events and real people, the characters created by the authors are fictional and their stories are a work of fiction.

Published in the UK by Scholastic Children's Books, 2020
Euston House, 24 Eversholt Street, London, NW1 1DB
A division of Scholastic Limited

London – New York – Toronto – Sydney – Auckland
Mexico City – New Delhi – Hong Kong

SCHOLASTIC and associated logos are trademarks and/or
registered trademarks of Scholastic Inc.

Foreword © Margaret Lynn Ltd, 2020
'Shipmates' and 'An End to Killing' © Tony Bradman, 2020
'Inglorious War' and 'Cracking Enemy Codes' © Jim Eldridge, 2020
'No More Seawater Soup' and 'We'll Meet Again' © Emily Hibbs, 2020
'Home From Home' and 'Just An Ordinary Day' © E.L. Norry, 2020
'Memories of Home' and 'A Sense of Home' © Bali Rai, 2020
'Tomorrow Today' and 'A World Away From Sanitary Street' © Leila Rasheed, 2020
'Fact File' text by Sue McMillan, Leah James and David James © Scholastic Children's Books, 2020

For picture credits see pages 158–9. Every effort has been made to ensure that this information is correct at the time of going to print. Any errors will be corrected upon reprint.

Trade edition ISBN 978 07023 0054 7
Schools market edition ISBN 978 07023 0314 2

A CIP catalogue record for this book is available from the British Library.

Printed in China

Papers used by Scholastic Children's Books are made from wood grown in sustainable forests.

1 3 5 7 9 10 8 6 4 2

www.scholastic.co.uk

HOME AGAIN

STORIES ABOUT COMING HOME FROM WAR

VE DAY

75TH ANNIVERSARY

Written by **Bali Rai**, **Leila Rasheed**, **Tony Bradman**,
Emily Hibbs, **Jim Eldridge** and **E.L. Norry**
Historical consultant: **Philip Parker**

SCHOLASTIC

CONTENTS

FOREWORD BY

DAME VERA LYNN

At first, it was hard to believe that the war was finally over. It had gone on for so long, and changed our lives in so many ways, that it felt almost unreal. At the time, I was travelling and could not join the celebrations as they spread across our country. I do remember, however, the tremendous sense of relief that washed over us and the sense of pride we felt, and still feel, in our brave boys. Victory had cost us all so much; so many gave their lives, and so many left home to risk everything for their country.

Home, I think, was such an important idea for us. It came to mean so much more than just the houses we lived in. Our entire country rallied together as one community, and as we lost loved ones, watched as our buildings were bombed and children were sent away, 'home' came to mean something more universal. It was the people we held dear, our Great British values and the wonderful heritage of our nation from its rich history to its natural beauty, including those famous white cliffs of Dover.

During that dark time, our homes were greatly shaken. We prevailed because we were united. That is, I think, something we can still learn from, and I hope that the memory of VE Day will always remind us to commemorate those who did so much, so that we could live the lives of freedom that we enjoy today.

Dame Vera Lynn

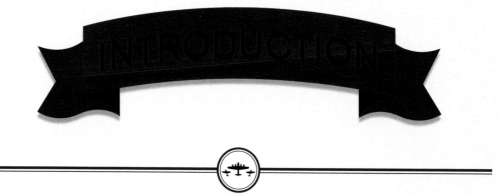

INTRODUCTION

VE Day or Victory in Europe Day marks the end of the fighting in Europe during the Second World War. Victory in Europe had been dear, with nearly 18 million service people killed on Europe's battlefields. This added up to nearly 11 million for the Allies (Britain, France, the Soviet Union and others) and over 7 million for the Axis powers (Germany, Italy and Japan). Britain lost over 380,000 members of the armed forces in Europe, while the Soviet Union had the greatest military loss with over 9 million killed.

Greater still was the effect on Europe's ordinary people, the civilians. Out of all those who died during the conflict in Europe, it is thought that out of a total of between 50 to 60 million deaths, 45 million were ordinary people.

During nearly six years of war, many peoples and nations came to Britain's aid from across the Commonwealth, Europe, North America and beyond. The Caribbean and Polish pilots who kept the skies safe, the Gurkhas and Indians who had fought up through Italy, and the Free French, American and Canadian soldiers who stormed the beaches of Normandy alongside British troops; the war in Europe was won by a powerful global collaboration.

With the announcement of Germany's surrender on 7 May 1945, crowds began gathering to celebrate in Britain and all over the world. The surrender came into effect the following day and, in Britain, 8 May was declared a national holiday.

VE Day saw celebrations across Britain with crowds joining together in public spaces, dancing and celebrating with people they'd never met before. The largest crowds were in London with up to 50,000 people gathering around Piccadilly Circus where American sailors formed a conga line with other merrymakers. Celebrations continued long into the night with dance halls and pubs staying open late.

Huge crowds went to Buckingham Palace, where King George VI, Queen Elizabeth and their daughters, Princess Elizabeth and Princess Margaret, waved from the balcony. During the evening, the princesses secretly made their way through the crowds below. The future Queen Elizabeth and her sister had been allowed to join the celebrations. Queen Elizabeth later recalled, "We stood outside and shouted, 'We want the King'… I think it was one of the most memorable nights of my life."

King George VI gave a radio address in which he paid tribute to those who could not join in the celebrations, saying: "Let us remember those who will not come back … let us remember the men in all the services, and the women in all the services, who have laid down their lives."

In July 1945, a general election was called that would shape post-war Britain. Although the war in Europe had ended, it continued in the Far East until August and Britain still felt its impact. Reeling from personal losses, and with ongoing shortages (clothes rationing lasted until 1949 and food rationing until 1954) and a need to rebuild their nation, Britain voted for Clement Attlee's Labour government to restore the country. Despite his wartime leadership, Winston Churchill was not returned to office. This change would bring about the creation of the welfare state and the National Health Service.

The UK celebrated VE Day with different events, such as parades, thanksgiving services and street parties. It was a day that brought communities together. St Paul's Cathedral, London, held ten back-to-back thanksgiving services, each one attended by over three thousand people. The celebrations were a mix of feelings; relief that the war in Europe was over and thanks that so many had come through it, mixed with sadness that so many had lost their lives and the understanding that the rebuilding of communities would now need to begin. A mood of thanksgiving, celebration and remembrance swept the UK and nations across the world.

VE Day celebrations in London, 8 May 1945

Left: crowds on VE Day in Toronto, Canada

Below: Winston Churchill waves to crowds in Whitehall, London as they celebrate VE Day, 8 May 1945

THE SECOND WORLD WAR IN NUMBERS

British and Commonwealth service people: 13 million

Largest Commonwealth force: India – 2.5 million volunteers

Prisoners of war (POWs) returned to the UK from Europe: 135,000

POWs returned to the UK from the Far East: 37,000

Jewish people freed from concentration camps: 300,000

Displaced people in Germany: 17 million

Refugees in Europe: 40 million

Refugees worldwide: 60 million

MEMORIES OF HOME

LANCE CORPORAL AJEET SINGH, AGED 34

BY BALI RAI

It was a yearning desire to go home. That is how I survived the war. The reason I emerged alive from the prisoner-of-war camps, the Stalags. That sounds obvious, peculiar even, but it is true. I meekly closed my eyes, forcibly held my tongue. Ignored the fear, bore the hardship. Wondered how my village had changed since my absence. What remained of the place I had left behind? I saw my resilient father tilling the soil in readiness for a new season, water buffalo pulling his plough. My beautiful mother beating clothes by the village pond, chatting with our neighbours. The glee of children frolicking barefoot in the dirt brought a smile. The swish of the evening breeze across the fields whispered lovingly in my ear. My senses remained filled with memories of home, to which I longed to return.

My time in Tobruk, Libya, was brutal. The Germans tormented us – the 11th Brigade of the 4th Infantry Division of the Indian Army – for eight months. The boom of the artillery guns. The persistent dread that each morning could be my last. The agony of perhaps never returning to the golden land of my birth. These things lacerated my soul, leaving scars that will not entirely heal. We resisted longer than any of us imagined. Until our ammunition ran dry, and the Germans broke through, forcing our surrender.

There was no shame in defeat. We had given our all, and although the enemy captured us, they could not break us. A Highland Regiment piper played as we were marched away. A tune of defiance. We were taken to Benghazi, left to wilt in the almost unbearable heat. We suffered and bled, and some of us died, but not once did I complain, or try to escape. I sought only to survive. Day after day under that desert sun, lacking shelter and real sustenance, all I thought of was my family and my home. I would not die under the African sun, I decided. I would not succumb to such a fate. My end lay in Punjab, the land of my forebears.

Eventually we were moved again, forced aboard a ship to Marseille in France. The voyage was cramped and dirty, yet still our morale was strong. We knew, even as we disembarked, that truth was on our side. The Germans taunted us, teased us, even beat us, but still we survived. After Marseille, I lost count of the places I saw. Stalag after

Stalag, until finally I was imprisoned somewhere between Hanover and Hamburg in Northern Germany.

The camp at Fallingbostel was as harsh as that in Libya. The only difference was the lack of searing heat. I was given a menial role to match my low rank. Forced to work in a paper mill, my days were long and weary, and my spirit weakened. The stench of the mill – comparable to rotten eggs and flatulence – did not lessen with familiarity. Nor did my eyes and nostrils get used to the itching, burning sensation from the chemicals they used.

My appearance caused a particular anger in the German guards. In surprisingly decent English, one questioned my loyalty to my colonial masters. I shook my head, unwilling to become a target, but the fellow persisted.

"It is my duty," I eventually told him. "As it was my father's. And my grandfather's before him. I am bound to it."

"But the British enslave your people and your lands," the guard said.

"And you would be so different?" I said. "I stand with my comrades without hesitation. For the greater good…"

"Whose greater good is this?" he asked.

"The world's," I replied.

His response came in German and was not friendly.

I grew weak and weary as time dragged on, comforted only by thoughts of home. In my exhausted state, I would often grow delirious and believe that I could smell my mother's cooking and taste fresh sugar cane juice. The grind of the pulping wheel, that sugary aroma, spices frying in melted butter, steaming fresh roti – these memories seemed real in those moments. They kept me sane, truth be told, bizarre as that may seem. They gave me a reason to go on. Something to look forward to.

And when war was over, and rescue came, I grew excited and impatient. Via Brussels, where we were shown great kindness and given wonderful hospitality, to an airbase in Buckinghamshire, as my British comrades cheered and laughed and grew merry, my own heart yearned for more. I was delighted to be alive and in England, but my soul ached for another place entirely. As I sat listening to the King's speech at exactly 7pm on VE Day, my thoughts were already far away.

You see, when the sun shines over Amritsar, the Golden Temple's gilded dome glistens like nothing else on Earth. The water that surrounds it, the sarovar, twinkles in the shimmering heat, and promises rebirth and refreshment to those who bathe in it. For a Sikh like me, no other place can compare. My love and respect for Britain and her people will always remain. My heart lies with my fallen comrades and those who survived alongside me. Our bond was born of sweat and tears, laughter and camaraderie; and in blood too. It cannot be broken. Yet still, I thirst for my home.

So, when I finally tread the dirt track past herds of water buffalo drinking at the village pool, I will be home. When I throw open the wooden gates to my house, and revel in my parents' embrace, I will be home. As the open fire crackles and milky tea boils, and my family gather to eat, I will be home. As I gaze into my mother's eyes, and feel her relief at regaining her son, I will be home.

For now, I must sit and wait...

THE INDIAN ARMY

As part of the Allied forces in the Second World War, the Indian Army fought alongside the major powers of Great Britain, France and the Soviet Union. As Britain still controlled most of India for the period of the war, the British Raj – the rulers of the British-held areas – sent Indian soldiers to reinforce the Allied troops.

At the height of the war, 2.5 million Indian soldiers were fighting against the Axis powers (Germany, Italy and Japan). They fought in Africa, Europe and Asia.

THE INDIAN ARMY IN NUMBERS

Lives lost: over 87,000

Wounded: over 34,000

Prisoners of war: over 65,000

Size at height of war: 2.5 million soldiers – the largest volunteer army in history

Medals won: 4,000 – including many Victoria Crosses (see page 137)

Infantrymen of the 2nd Battalion, 7th Rajput Regiment in Burma, 1943

THE SIEGE OF TOBRUK

In 1941, Germany pushed forward into Libya to attempt capture of the Allied-held port of Tobruk. Australian forces had captured the town from Italy in January, but from April until August, they were trapped there, resisting the Germans.

In August, British – including Indian – soldiers, and Polish troops gradually took over from the Australians. Then, in December, after eight months of constant air raids and attacks, the Germans finally broke though the Allied defences and took back control of Tobruk for the Axis powers.

Above right: men of the King's Own Regiment man a Vickers machine gun at Tobruk, 10 November 1941
Left: a soldier of the Polish Independent Carpathian Rifles Brigade shares a joke with an Australian fellow soldier, 1941

PRISONER-OF-WAR CAMPS IN EUROPE

More than 170,000 British prisoners were captured by the Axis powers in the Second World War. They were put into prisoner-of-war (POW) camps. Perhaps the most famous of these was Colditz Castle in Germany, then known as Oflag IVC.

Colditz was a POW camp for Allied officers; especially those who had tried to escape from other camps. Set high on a hill, Colditz was famously difficult to break out of. Before the US Army freed the prisoners in 1945, thirty-two prisoners had successfully got away.

THE GENEVA CONVENTIONS

- A set of four agreements between nearly all the countries of the world
- The Geneva Conventions lay out rules for the fair treatment of POWs in times of conflict
- The POWs protected under the rules can be civilians as well as members of the armed forces
- After the first convention in 1863, the International Committee of the Red Cross was formed – nearly every country in the world has a Red Cross or Red Crescent society, which provides humanitarian aid in times of need.

Senior POW
Allied officers
in front of the
Colditz Castle
chapel

Colditz Castle
circa WW2,
taken by an
American GI

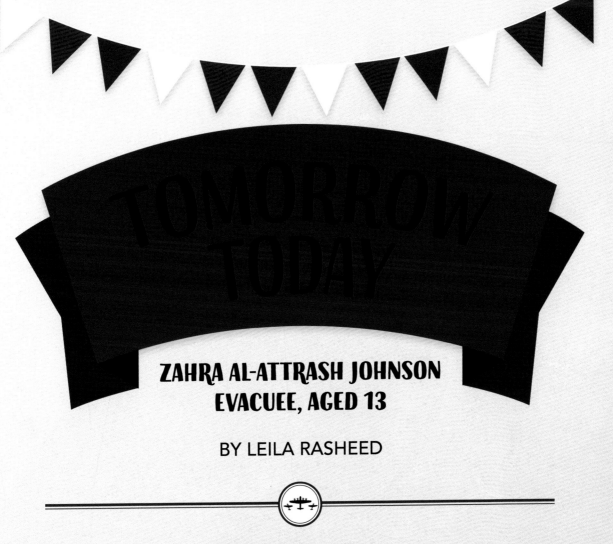

TOMORROW TODAY

ZAHRA AL-ATTRASH JOHNSON
EVACUEE, AGED 13

BY LEILA RASHEED

SEPTEMBER 1939

The clouds were thick with rain when we finally got to Cambridge. The train stopped and we all tumbled out on to the platform. Mo, my little brother, clung onto my hand. He was only five, and the label around his neck was almost as big as he was.

I didn't know where to go or what to do, and I couldn't see our teacher anywhere in the crowd. I looked around, trying not to show how scared I was. There were some grown-ups at the end of the platform, looking at the children in front of them as if they were goods in a shop. I realized the grown-ups must be the kind strangers the teacher had told us we were going to stay with. I didn't really understand why; I thought it must be a type of a holiday, like when we went hop picking. *Maybe*, I thought, it was to make up for the war.

When there were only a few children left, a woman with a kind, plump face arrived, arm-in-arm with an older man. It was hard to see his eyes through his thick glasses.

"And what's your name, dear?" the woman said, looking down at me.

"Zahra Al-Attrash Johnson," I said shyly.

"You're an Arab?" The man's eyebrows shot up from behind his glasses.

"M-my father's Egyptian, sir."

"Hmm, that makes a difference." He said something to me that I didn't understand at all, but it sounded like Arabic. My mind went blank and I could only think of one thing: thank you. "*Shokran?*"

He laughed. "I can see you're more of a cockney than an Arab. I am Professor Blythe. I teach oriental studies at Cambridge University."

I must have looked completely blank, because he sighed.

"Very well, come along."

To my horror, I realized he meant just me – not Mo.

"I can't leave my brother, sir!"

His face fell. "We really don't want a small child. I need peace and quiet to work."

Mo's mouth dropped open in shock and he started to wail. Professor Blythe put his hands over his ears.

"Mum said we weren't to be separated!" I said desperately. "Shush, Mo, please!"

"Dear, we can't split them up," Mrs Blythe protested. "Just think, these poor children have already had to leave their mother at the mercy of bombs—"

"Bombs?" I said. It was the first I'd heard of it. Mrs Blythe's eyes widened; she clearly hadn't realized that no one had told us. "I have to go back to Mum and Dad!" I pulled away, but Mrs Blythe stopped me. She crouched down and spoke to me gently.

"Your parents won't want you to go back. They want you to be safe until all this is over. You can both stay with us." She cast a sharp glance at the professor. "And that's that."

And so we moved in with Professor and Mrs Blythe, in their enormous house near Cambridge. They were both kind, although I had no idea how to answer all the questions the professor had about Islam. He seemed very interested in the fact that we went to each other's houses for Friday prayers because there was no mosque.

"That's a shame. Perhaps when this war is over, we can do something about it," he said.

At school, the teacher raised her eyebrows when I told her my name.

"Zahra Al-Attrash Johnson? Goodness, I don't think it's very fair to expect us to say that every day. Sarah Johnson will do."

"No one in my old school minded my name," I protested.

"That was the East End," she sniffed.

So I became Sarah Johnson, half of me washed away as if it was dirty. Luckily a few other children from my street were put in the same class as me, and they kept on calling me Zahra. It was funny: at school I had to pretend I wasn't Egyptian at all, but at the Blythes' I felt I had to pretend I was more Egyptian than I really was. It was confusing. I just wanted to go home and see my mum and dad again. I was frightened that they would get bombed while I was away, and I would never see them again. My father walked with sticks after an accident, and I had horrible nightmares where he was struggling to get out of the house when a bomb hit it.

In the end, there was no bombing. A few months later we were all put back on the train and sent home to London.

"You will make sure to write, won't you?" said Mrs Blythe as she waved us off, and the professor shook Mo's hand and called him a 'brave little man'.

But we never wrote. Almost as soon as we arrived home, just as if the Germans had been waiting for us, the bombing began.

September 1940

My first bomb blew out the windows in my bedroom and rammed a spear of wood deep into the wall. After that, there were bombs every night. We stuck it out as long as we could, but on 12 September my mother said, "I'm not staying here to be Jerry's target. Get your coats, kids, we're going to the Tube station."

So along we went, my father hobbling on his sticks and my mum carrying Mo wrapped up in a blanket. It was freezing and the night smelled of burning. Down in the Tube station we realized everyone else had had the same idea. At first it was like an adventure, sleeping on the tracks. One lady had brought her knitting and another one told jokes. I had fun – until I heard the explosions outside and the sirens. Then everyone went dead quiet.

There were fifty-seven nights of bombing. Our school was closed to be turned into a military depot. My mother tried to teach us all a bit when she had time but she was busy because she was a nurse, and my father was working on the docks. So we just ran loose. We climbed the ruins of bombed-out houses and collected bits of German shells. Death became normal.

And then, in 1941, St-Mary-le-Bow was hit. The bells crashed to the ground and the church went up in flames. My mum and dad were in tears.

"How long do you think the war will go on?" I said to my mum the next day.

"It'll have to go on till we win it," she said shortly.

No one said, but I thought: *Maybe we won't win it. Maybe they will.*

May 1945

One Monday night, the grown-ups were like a flock of birds, twittering with news that I didn't understand. Mo and I took advantage of it to eat as much as we could – we were having beef, which was a rare treat. Then after dinner, my father told everyone to be quiet and switched on the radio. A voice as posh as the Blythes' came on and told us that Germany was surrendering.

My mother gasped and my father banged his walking sticks on the ground.

"At last," was all he said. "We did it, kids. It's over. No more bombs."

But that very night I was woken up by sirens and explosions. I sat bolt upright, shaking uncontrollably.

"You said no more bombs!" I screamed.

My father came in and opened the curtains. Outside, the sky was lit up by searchlights – only, I realized, they weren't searchlights. It was lightning, the crash was thunder, and the sirens were our ships on the River Thames, celebrating. For the first time, I could believe the war was over.

The next day was a holiday. The sun was shining and we joined the neighbours, putting up decorations and getting ready for a street party. Someone had a gramophone out, playing: "There'll be bluebirds over the white cliffs of Dover... tomorrow, when the world is free."

"It's tomorrow today!" said Mo. "The war's over and we're free."

Later, Dad took me and Mo into the city. On the bus, we peered out of the window to see what was going on. Another bus drove up alongside us, honking its horn. A banner on it read: 'This is the bus that Hitler missed.' The passengers were laughing and singing. In Trafalgar Square we saw a couple of Land Girls dancing in the fountains with the sailors. One of them slipped, and fell into the water, whooping with laughter.

"Everyone's gone mad!" said Dad, but it was a lovely sort of madness, with parties and music and tears of joy everywhere. Later, we went to see Winston Churchill giving a speech at the Ministry of Health, and cheered until our throats were sore.

When Big Ben struck nine, my dad said it was time to go home.

"It's still light!" Mo protested.

"But there's work for me in the morning," Dad said with a smile, "and school for you."

As we walked to the bus stop, I saw a very familiar couple strolling along the Embankment.

"That's Professor Blythe!" I said. I ran up to them and tugged at the professor's sleeve. He looked at me astonished, then smiled.

"Why, it's Zahra!" Mrs Blythe exclaimed. "How wonderful it is to see you!"

My father was shy at first, but he was delighted when the professor spoke Arabic to him, and asked how the mosque was coming along. "We are so glad that the war is finally over," he said.

Mrs Blythe smiled sadly. "Our son is still in the Far East. It won't be over for us until he is safe home again. Then we will have to think about what we do next – all of us."

After we said our goodbyes and we had got on to a bus, I couldn't stop thinking about what Mrs Blythe had said. The bombing was over, but the fighting was still going on, far away. Yes, it was tomorrow, and half of the world was free, but what about the future?

What did you do when there wasn't a war on?

I would have to start finding out.

EVACUEES

In Britain, at the start of September 1939, more than 3 million people were moved or 'evacuated' to the safety of the countryside from cities and towns that might be bombed.

Most evacuees were schoolchildren and their teachers, but some mothers and children under five also went.

The parents of children being evacuated were given a list of things the children needed to take with them:

Gas mask

One overcoat or mackintosh

One pullover or jersey

One shirt with collar

Two pairs of socks

One pair of trousers (long or short)

One vest

One pair of pants

Handkerchiefs

One pair boots or shoes

One pair plimsolls

A comb

Toothbrush

Face cloth

Towel

Stationery

Bible

EVACUATION IN NUMBERS

Code name: Operation Pied Piper

Began: 1 September 1939

Officially ended: March 1946

Numbers evacuated: 3,000,000

Also evacuated: art and other national treasures, the Bank of England, some BBC productions

Child evacuees board a bus from
Bristol to Devon

ANDERSON SHELTERS

C hildren who were not evacuated or who returned home before bombing began may well have had to take cover in an Anderson shelter during air raids. When the war started, thousands of Anderson shelters were delivered to homes around the country.

The shelters were made of corrugated steel and designed to be built in a pit about 1 metre (3 feet) deep and covered with earth to provide extra protection.

Anderson shelters could sleep up to six people, but the metal boosted the sound of the bombs exploding and in winter they were freezing cold, damp and some flooded. Some families chose to have a Morrison shelter instead – this indoor shelter was a metal dining table that families could crawl under during air raids. Both types of shelter saved many lives.

In London, people who didn't have shelters at home took to sleeping in Underground stations and the caves at Chislehurst, while others made use of cellars, railway arches and even church crypts.

Right: children climb into their garden Anderson shelter in London, 1940

Left: an Anderson shelter in Poplar, East London, after a land mine fell nearby

THE BLITZ

In September 1940, Hitler decided to force Britain to surrender by bombing towns and cities to destroy ports, dockyards and factories. When the air raid sirens wailed in the afternoon of 7 September, an estimated 1,000 planes that were headed to London from Germany launched an attack that became known as 'Black Saturday'. It was the start of the Blitz, which lasted until May 1941.

During the Blitz, London was bombed for more than fifty-seven nights in a row. The Nazis also bombed other cities around Britain. Over the course of the war, the Allies attacked many German cities, including Cologne, Hamburg and Dresden.

THE BLITZ IN NUMBERS

Began: 7 September 1940
Bombs dropped over London (tons): an estimated 18,000
Civilians killed: over 40,000
Civilians injured: over 80,000
People made homeless: 2,250,000
Longest continual bombing: 57 nights
Other cities hit: Belfast, Birmingham, Bristol, Cardiff, Coventry, Glasgow, Hull, Leeds, Liverpool, Manchester, Portsmouth, Sheffield, Southampton Swansea

Burnt-out buildings during the Blitz

INGLORIOUS WAR

BOMBARDIER JOHN MCCONNELL, AGED 24

BY JIM ELDRIDGE

Bombardier John McConnell stood with his unit – the 63rd Anti-Tank Regiment – watching as hundreds of unarmed German soldiers filed past the checkpoint in the small village just outside Kiel, Germany. Some marched, boots stamping, arms swinging defiantly, but most shuffled helplessly along. It was 8 May 1945, and for these defeated soldiers the war was over.

That morning, Germany had surrendered. Some of the Germans approached the watching British, hands above their heads, pleading to be allowed to surrender and be taken prisoner. All were refused and told, "*Nein*. Go."

John knew why they were desperate to surrender – they were starving and hoped the Allies would feed them. *Fat chance of that,* thought John sourly. *We've barely got enough for ourselves.* There'd been no bread for three weeks. The celebration breakfast that morning for John and his comrades had consisted of tinned sardines, pilchards and powdered potatoes. There hadn't even been any beer for them to toast the fact the war was finally over.

Watching the Germans trudge past, John bore in mind what the padre, the army priest, had told him about feeling sympathy for them. "They are human beings, just like you. They did the same job, but for the other side. They are no different to you. Give them your compassion."

But that was something John found very hard to do. The German soldiers responsible for what the 63rd Regiment had discovered when they entered the Bergen-Belsen concentration camp just three weeks before were nothing like him, or anyone else he knew.

It had been on 12 April that German SS military officers had come out of the Bergen-Belsen camp as the British 11th Armoured Division approached it. They were waving a white flag and they told the British soldiers that they wanted to negotiate a truce, and also surrender the camp. It was for displaced persons, they informed the soldiers. The problem was there was an outbreak of typhus in there. Because of this, the SS advised against entering the camp. They warned against letting the inmates out for fear they would spread typhus among the local civilian population. The SS also wanted safe passage for their own people. After some hours of talking an agreement was reached in the early hours of 13 April: most of the SS people would be allowed to leave, but the officer in charge would remain, along with the regular German and Hungarian soldiers, who would guard the outside.

Heavy fighting in the area delayed the arrival of the rest of the British forces and their Canadian allies, and it was the afternoon of 15 April before the Allies were able to enter the camp. John and a unit of the 63rd were among those entering. What they found inside Belsen shocked John to the core – he thought he'd already seen everything bad that this war could produce.

The camp was a nightmare: 60,000 inmates in striped pyjamas, more skeleton than human, most of them dying of sickness and starvation. The stench of death was everywhere from those who'd already died, their bodies rotting where they fell. John discovered that the majority were Jewish, along with about 20,000 Soviet soldiers who'd been taken as prisoners of war, but it took time to discover this because the SS had destroyed most of the camp's files before they left.

They finally got the information from the camp chief officer because he seemed eager to appease the Allies who'd arrived in the hope of being granted his freedom. Those prisoners who could walk, desperate for food and relieved that the camp had been liberated, tried to break into the stores in an effort to get food, but – to the shock of John and the other Allied soldiers – were gunned down and killed by some of the German and Hungarian guards. The British shot those guards in their turn, and only then did the other guards hand in their weapons.

Over the next few weeks the British and Canadian troops worked hard to provide medical assistance and food, but even so the inmates were dying at a rate of hundreds per day. So many dead bodies were piling up, increasing the risk of typhus spreading, that the British ordered the German guards and those few SS men who'd remained to dig mass graves to bury the dead. At first the SS refused, but when rifles were pointed at them, they reluctantly complied.

After two weeks John and the 63rd were moved on to Kiel, leaving the 11th Armoured behind to continue the work at Belsen. But the images of what he'd seen during his time there were burnt into John's memory. That was why, even though this was supposed to be a day of victory, or celebration, there was no such feeling of victory or joy in John's heart. War was not glorious.

THE HOLOCAUST

The Holocaust was when millions of Jewish people were murdered, simply because of their identity. Adolf Hitler and his Nazi party led this mass murder.

The Jewish people were Hitler's main target – an estimated 6 million, including 1 million children, were murdered. This is thought to be 7 out of 10 of all Jews in Europe at the time.

Hitler's idea of 'an Aryan master race' – those with white skin, light hair and light eyes – also meant that millions of other ordinary citizens were targeted and killed. This included Jehovah's Witnesses, people with disabilities, Roma people, people of colour and LGBT people.

Nazi forces imprisoned these groups in concentration camps, such as Auschwitz and Bergen-Belsen. These were large prison camps where people were treated terribly, many dying from starvation or illness. People were often murdered in these camps as soon as they arrived.

The total amount of innocent civilians murdered by the Nazi regime is thought to be 17 million. The Holocaust was a genocide – the mass killing of a group of people because of their identity.

TIMELINE OF THE HOLOCAUST

January 1933 Adolf Hitler of the Nazi Party appointed as German chancellor

1933 The Nazi regime opens the first concentration camps in Germany

1939–40 Germany invades Poland, taking away the property and the rights of Jewish people there

1942–45 The extermination of Jewish people and other minorities intensifies

April–May 1945 As the Axis powers retreat, the Allies discover the concentration camps and realize the full horror of Nazi crimes against ordinary people

1945–53 Many Holocaust survivors were placed in 'displaced persons camps' where they lived until a new home was found for them. The last camp closed in 1953.

The liberation of the Bergen-Belsen concentration camp, April 1945 – British soldiers supervise the distribution of food to camp inmates

The Holocaust Memorial in Berlin, Germany

A SENSE OF HOME

FRED CASTLE
AIR RAID WARDEN, AGED 46

BY BALI RAI

I had saved a bottle of whisky for that day. A special treat to mark the conclusion of that terrible time. They called it VE Day and, as it dawned, the shattered and grubby streets of Whitechapel, London, seemed a little brighter. A little more hopeful. We'd known that the end was coming. Read the news of Germany's collapse and Hitler's death. Cheered as our boys entered Berlin alongside the Americans. It was finally over. Six years of pain and fear, darkness and death. Both my older sons were at war, so I had another reason to rejoice. They'd be home soon, safe and sound.

I dressed, and then woke my daughter and we left the house early. I was a butcher by trade and needed to open. It was a national holiday, but Mr Churchill had asked that shopkeepers opened for a few hours. People would want supplies for the parties they'd planned. Celebrations to mark the end of war. Not that there was much to be had. Rationing was still in place and even though a little more food was getting through, on VE Day all I had left was some beef.

Well, not all. I'd hoarded some meat pies, truth be told. And our neighbours had banded together too. Whatever we could find in those unusual times. Sugar and tea, lard and eggs, cobbled together from rations. Even jelly – but don't ask me where that came from. I don't think people really understand how tough things were back then. You had to be there to know. Times were hard and Whitechapel took a pounding from the Nazis. I know. I was an air raid warden as well as a butcher.

I still hear the V-1 rockets whining as they fell. 'Doodlebugs' we called them. They terrified some and made others furious. Three nights a week, I walked the streets of Whitechapel, calling out to those ignoring the blackout. It happened more than you would imagine. Often by mistake, but sometimes through idiocy or drunkenness.

"Put that light out!" I'd often cry.

"Cover that window!" I'd sometimes yell.

The damage was extensive at first – homes and businesses burning, people left with nothing but the clothes in which they stood. Often, after a night of destruction, I'd be tasked with searching the rubble, or entering damaged houses carrying a pike – a long wooden pole that allowed me to prod the ceilings to ensure any loose sections didn't crush me. It was a dirty and dangerous job, but I didn't mind it. I was too old for the Second World War, having fought in the First. Being a warden was my duty, and I was proud to do my bit. We all were, no matter what we did. The war effort required it and we did not complain.

So, VE Day was a time to celebrate. The war was won, our troops were coming home and peace had come home too. The street parties would be make-do affairs – just like everything else back then. We learned to survive, to make the best of what we had. Lemons and lemonade, and all that. Not that you could find a lemon back then.

My customers started queuing early. Neighbours and friends, regulars and strangers too. They waited without complaining, offered up their coupons and took away their share. There was joy in those voices, hope in those faces, and it made my heart sing. I imagined the shop full to the rafters again – no more rationing, no more shortages. Sausages and pies, and prime cuts of lamb and beef rather than whatever was left over, and maybe some game birds too. I longed to be a proper butcher again. To put away my blue air raid warden's overalls forever.

I did not want to see another gas mask, nor search through rubble for poor innocents that might have survived a dreadful night of devastation. I had seen my share of death. It was inevitable. VE Day marked the end of that nightmare. Sunrise on a new day. A homecoming of all sorts. Peace, life, happiness and normality. That morning, in my shop, people were smiling properly again and walked with a spring in their step. I saw relief; I saw optimism returned.

Everything seemed airier and lighter, and the colours brighter.

The street party was a sight to behold. We set up trestle tables, and my neighbours found bunting, Union Jack flags and even a rare balloon or two. We had eggless fruitcake and jelly, and whatever tea we could find, and my meat pies were very welcome and scoffed quickly. We made beef dripping or corned beef sandwiches, and Lord Woolton pies from any vegetables we could find. The local pub ran dry of beer well before the 10.30pm curfew, and a parade of sozzled folk sang songs and told jokes, as the children played all around us.

A sudden bang, and then another... I jumped from my seat, panicked and concerned. My wife's hand caught my arm.

"Calm down, Fred. It's just fireworks, you daft old man!"

The crowds around us roared with approval and my panic subsided. Fireworks, of course. What else would they be? My wife smiled and offered me some fruitcake.

"Better get home..."

We did our share of tidying up, said goodnight to our neighbours and headed indoors. My daughter was still excited and loud, but we soon packed her off to bed. And once there, she fell right to sleep. Finally, I sat and cracked open my special whisky. Poured a large measure and took in the aroma, before savouring the taste. I sat back and closed my eyes for a moment. For the first time in years, I was truly at peace. No air raids, no burning houses, no distraught and destitute families. Just a sense of calm. A sense of home, returning.

FOOD RATIONING

With food in short supply, the UK government had to find a way to make sure that what they did have was shared out fairly.

In January 1940, bacon, butter and sugar became the first foods to be rationed. By 1942, most foods were rationed and others were hard to find. People were given ration books and had to register with their local shops, where the shopkeepers marked every purchase in their ration book.

Right: a child's ration book

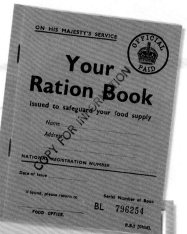

A TYPICAL WEEKLY RATION FOR AN ADULT

All conversions are approximate.

- 50 g (2 oz) butter
- 100 g (4 oz) cooking fat/lard
- 225 g (8 oz) sugar
- 50 g (2 oz) cheese
- meat to the value of 1 shilling and six pence – between 350–450 g (12 oz–1 lb)
- 1 fresh egg
- 100 g (4 oz) bacon or ham

- 100 g (4 oz) margarine
- 1,200 ml (2 pints) milk
- 50 g (2 oz) tea

PLUS:

- 16 points per month to 'spend' on whatever they wanted such as tinned food, dried fruit and cereals
- 1 packet of 12 dried eggs every four weeks
- 350 g (12 oz) sweets every four weeks
- 450 g (1 lb) jam every two months

SO WHAT DID EVERYONE EAT?

During the war, people needed recipes and ideas to make food stretch as far as possible. Cookery books and magazines printed ideas for some rather unusual concoctions, such as 'mock crab', which contained dried egg, salad cream, cheese, but no crab!

There were strict rules about dining out, too. Menus were limited to three courses and there was a maximum charge of five shillings. This meant that restaurants had to serve smaller portions or cheaper food to make a profit. Fortunately, fish and chips weren't rationed and this quickly became something that everyone enjoyed.

Carrots became a staple food during the war. They were nutritious, could be grown at home and were naturally sweet. Carrots were often used instead of sugar in recipes such as cakes so the family's precious sugar ration could be used for other things.

To get people to eat more carrots, propaganda posters were made which said they could help you to see in the blackout. Some shopkeepers even popped carrots on sticks and sold them as substitute ice lollies!

The 'Dig for Victory' campaign encouraged people to grow vegetables and fruit at home and in allotments created in public spaces. Across the country, lawns, tennis courts and even golf courses disappeared to be replaced by neat rows of crops. Leaflets were made giving step-by-step instructions on digging and planting seeds and people were also encouraged to keep chickens and pigs.

Left: allotments in Kensington Gardens, London, 1942

53

NO MORE SEAWATER SOUP

CORA LE PROVOST
POSTMISTRESS, AGED 35

BY EMILY HIBBS

Cora was sending one of her imaginary telegrams. As soon as Charlie pushed open the door to the Smith Street Post Office, he heard the *click-click-click* of her fingers against the counter. Cora paused mid-message and looked up.

"Are you writing to Kitty?" Charlie asked. Although the telegraph line had been cut almost five years ago, Cora still liked to put together make-believe messages that nobody would ever receive. Practising Morse code, the secret language used to tap out telegrams, kept her mind busy, and helped to pass the time in a post office that often didn't have customers for days. Usually, the messages were for her daughter, Kitty, but it also cheered Cora up to send little notes of advice to important men like Winston Churchill or King George VI. Once or twice, she'd even written an imaginary message to Adolf Hitler, asking not so politely that he tell his soldiers to clear off and leave Guernsey alone. She knew the telegrams weren't real, but they made her feel better.

"Yes, that one was for Kitty," Cora replied. "I asked her if she'd read any good books lately and told her to bring you back a souvenir when she comes home. Nothing big – just a conker or a pebble or something."

"I wouldn't mind a conker from England," Charlie said thoughtfully. "But I'd prefer some soap. Or some chocolate!"

"I doubt they've got any more chocolate over there than we have here," Cora said with a smile.

Charlie shrugged. "I bet Kitty will be nearly as tall as me now."

Cora reckoned Kitty would be taller, though she didn't say anything. Charlie was nearly eleven, and Kitty nine, but he had barely grown since the start of the war and was as skinny and ashen as driftwood. Though life in England was sure to be hard, Cora hoped her daughter had enough to eat, at least. Here on the island, flour had run out months ago, most of the livestock had been requisitioned to feed German troops in France and salt had become so scarce that many islanders sloshed seawater into their soups for flavour.

"Mum told me to take you for a walk," Charlie said. "She didn't like the idea of you tapping away to yourself in here, waiting for Mr Churchill's announcement."

Charlie's mum, Elspeth, was Cora's next-door neighbour. She knew that Cora missed Kitty terribly, and often sent Charlie on missions to cheer up her friend.

Cora allowed herself to be tugged from behind the counter, out of the post office and down the hill towards the seafront. She was cheered to spot Union Jacks waving from a few windows. Yesterday, Cora and Charlie had huddled round Elspeth's secret wireless – one of the few radios the Germans hadn't managed to confiscate – to hear the news that the Allies had accepted the Nazis' surrender. That the war was finally, finally over. But Cora couldn't quite believe it. She was trying not to get her hopes up, just in case it all came to nothing.

They stopped as close to the sea as they dared and stared out.

What a lot of horrors this harbour has seen, Cora thought. First, there was the week the children had left. After France had fallen to the Nazis, the British government had decided they were unable to defend the Channel Islands. Ships had come to take the children to England for the duration of the war, but the islanders only had one day's notice. A day to decide whether to send their children far away, to a country that might end up in just as much danger as Guernsey, or to keep them close and watch them suffer through the inevitable Nazi occupation. Cora had decided Kitty should go; Elspeth chose for Charlie to stay. Cora knew that they both wished they'd made the other choice.

A week after the children had left, the Germans bombed Saint Peter Port, and two days after that, the first of the Nazi soldiers arrived by air. The occupation of Guernsey had begun. Charlie, then just six years old, was determined to singlehandedly run the Germans off the island.

"I'm going to fight them all," he had told Cora and Elspeth stubbornly, raising his fists, "and take Guernsey back!"

But as the rows of uniformed men swept through the town, Cora's heart grew heavy.

"You may as well borrow a broom and start sweeping sand off the beach," she'd told him quietly.

The Germans had built fortifications, miles of underground tunnels and gun emplacements surrounding the island. They had enforced strict rules, including curfews that kept changing, and claimed many of the islanders' homes as their own. Worst of all, they had brought over thousands of slave workers from Eastern Europe; gaunt shadows forced to work on the construction projects. The first time Charlie had seen them, hunched and huddled, he'd reached for Cora's fingers and gripped them tightly, even though he'd told her he was too old for holding hands.

Now, nearly five years later, it looked like the occupation was ending.

"Kitty will be sailing back into this harbour soon," Charlie said in that confident way of his. Cora was quiet. Squinting at the water in just the right way, she could pretend the events of the last five years had never happened. She could ignore the curls of barbed wire and the huge *VERBOTEN* signs, and look out at the light glittering on the water, the waves foaming like frothed milk. The Germans may have taken the radios and cameras, the pigs and cows, but one thing they couldn't steal from the islanders was the sea. It was bigger than Hitler, bigger than the Nazis, bigger than this war. The sea was there before, and it would be there after.

"Come on," said Charlie, turning away from the harbour. "I reckon it's about time for the announcement."

They set off back into town. The hilly streets of Saint Peter Port hummed with people; islanders buzzing with nervous energy and soldiers shuffling from place to place. At three o'clock, Churchill's voice rang from the loudspeakers, confirming that the fighting really was over. A cheer, deafening as a thunderclap, broke out at the words "...and our dear Channel Islands are also to be freed today." Cora smiled as Charlie punched the air.

The following day, Cora, Charlie and Elspeth lined up along the harbour wall with hundreds of others. There had been some confusion as to what was going on; when the Germans would leave, when the British would arrive. But finally, a navy vessel sailed into the port and twenty or so British soldiers clambered out on to the jetty. The crowd tumbled forwards to embrace them. Charlie gave a whoop as one of the uniformed men slipped a thin bar of chocolate into his hand.

"Look, Cora!" he cried, waving the bar at her before shoving the whole thing into his mouth. They followed the parade of people waving Union Jacks back into the town. As the church bells clanged, the crowd broke into an emotional chorus of 'God Save the King'.

Cora slipped away, the noise fading as she navigated the narrow streets. She was happy Guernsey was free, happy the fighting had finished, happy there would be no more seawater soup. Still, for her, the war couldn't truly be over until another boat pulled into the harbour — one carrying her daughter. The door of the post office clattered open and Cora went back to her desk. Soon, the line would be repaired, and she'd be back to writing real telegrams. But for now, she had another imaginary message to send:

Darling Kitty. The island is liberated. I can't wait for you to come home.

OCCUPATION OF
THE CHANNEL ISLANDS

The Channel Islands were the only part of the British Isles to be seized by Nazi Germany. The British government had demilitarized the islands due to concerns over the safety of the residents. The occupation began on 19 June 1940.

During the German rule, there were petrol shortages, radios were taken away, food was scarce, and the islands were moved to match the time of Central Europe – an hour ahead of the rest of Britain.

On 9 May 1945, surrender papers were signed by the German commander in chief at dawn aboard HMS *Bulldog*.

The 9 May is now celebrated across the islands as Liberation Day – the day that the British Task Force came to free the islands from German rule.

The German Commander-in-Chief of the Channel Islands (on the right) arrives at HMS *Bulldog* to sign the surrender document

Right-hand page: crowds gathered in Guernsey to welcome the British Task Force sent to liberate the island

DUNKIRK

The Nazis were using a new style of rapid fighting called 'Blitzkrieg' (lightning war). Bombers attacked from the air, while tanks and troops smashed their way through ground defences. In just six weeks they invaded Belgium, the Netherlands and Luxembourg. France was next.

With the Nazi army moving across France, the Allies were pushed north where thousands of soldiers were stranded on the coast at Dunkirk. If they weren't rescued, the Allies would have to surrender.

A daring evacuation mission began. Hundreds of vessels crossed the Channel to ferry the soldiers to safety, while RAF planes battled Nazi Stukas in the skies overhead. As well as Navy destroyers and minesweepers, there were many 'little ships' involved in the rescue from fishing boats and sailing yachts to lifeboats and barges, all crewed by brave volunteers.

DUNKIRK IN NUMBERS

Code name: Operation Dynamo

Also known as: The Miracle of Dunkirk

Soldiers rescued: 338,000

Time taken: 9 days from 27 May to 4 June 1940

Rescue vessels: more than 900

Most soldiers rescued in a day: 68,014 on 31 May

Ships lost: 236

Smallest boat: *Tamzine*, a 4.4-metre fishing boat

Officers of the Royal Ulster Rifles awaiting evacuation at Bray Dunes near Dunkirk, May 1940

HOME FROM HOME

ISAAC ROSENBERG
KINDERTRANSPORT CHILD, AGED 15

BY E.L. NORRY

I jerk awake, the image of glass raining from the sky fresh in my mind. I lie still for a moment, staring at the off-white painted ceiling of my bedroom, until my thumping heart slows down.

It's all right, Isaac – calm down. You're safe, I remind myself.

The same nightmare four or five nights a week: shards of glass pouring from the Berlin sky. I dart to avoid the splinters and Papa and Mama are ripped from each other's arms. She beats her fists against a black overcoat, but Papa's dragged through crowds and bundled on to a truck. Taken away to one of the camps. The camps that no one ever returns from.

My back is slippery with sweat against the sheets.

Perhaps Papa escaped. Or fought back. He might have been rescued.

My ragged breathing returns to normal. That night of smashed shop windows and synagogues set ablaze, Stars of David streaked in paint on doors and banging black boots marching on cobbles, with echoes of "Dirty Jew" thrown around like a curse… it's over. That was seven years ago.

I'm safe.

The Refugee Children's Movement rescued thousands of children. I was brought to London and the Cohens were kind enough to take me in. They're Jewish too, but they don't speak any German, and this isn't my home.

I had a home. I have parents. Somewhere, still.

When I first arrived, my parents sent me letters. Life was getting harder in Berlin, they said. But the last letter was three years ago. Mrs Cohen says not to give up hope, but with no photographs, I can barely remember their faces. I think that's why the nightmares started – to help me remember. Even though I often wake up crying, at least their kind brown eyes are clear and bright for a few moments.

Mama sang like an angel. Does she still?

After getting dressed, I take out the envelope I keep safe under my pillow. My stamp collection is the only possession I brought from home. My favourite stamps are of the 1936 Olympic Games that Papa gave me. They show the best of my country, what we excelled at and believed was worth celebrating. Not the Berlin we see now, full of anger and hatred. I gaze at my stamps, the only connection to my parents, my home and my language.

In the living room, at 3pm, Mr and Mrs Cohen sit on the sofa, hands clasped, listening intently to the radio on the sideboard.

"Come, Isaac dear, listen!" Mrs Cohen says, indicating the armchair opposite the fireplace. Mrs Cohen smiles a lot, with blue eyes crinkly at the corners. I speak English, but the shapes feel awkward in my mouth. Although the language of kindness is one I can always understand.

A voice I recognize comes from the radio. The prime minister, Winston Churchill, announces, "We may allow ourselves a brief period of rejoicing, but let us not forget for a moment the toil and efforts that lie ahead."

Mr and Mrs Cohen stare at each other. Mrs Cohen suddenly puts a hand over her mouth and a sob pops out.

"It's over!" she cries.

Mr Cohen squeezes her hand and then embraces her tightly.

Over? Excited but confused, I look from one to the other. "Does this mean no more war?" I ask, hopefully.

"In Europe, yes," Mr Cohen says, smiling, though his sparkling eyes dull as he adds, "The Far East is another matter entirely."

No more fighting? Has Germany lost?

Hope sneaks into cracks it had long ago abandoned.

What does this mean for my people? Will we no longer be spat at in the street? Will I be able to go home? Will I once again hear Mama sing?

***

After tea and some fruitcake that Mrs Cohen had been saving, she says, "Isaac, a young boy like you ought to be out and about, celebrating with others. There'll be a knees-up in town, I'm sure. Why don't you go and see while I get supper ready?"

Piccadilly Circus is crammed full of people. The air is buzzing with cheering and laughter as young men swing ladies around, their skirts flaring. There's hardly space to breathe. Everywhere I turn, smiling faces look back at me. People hang off lampposts, giddy with the news that the fighting is over.

The centre podium, where Anteros usually stands – Mrs Cohen said the statue was removed when the Blitz began – is surrounded by posters advertising savings stamps. People on the top wave flags, throwing kisses and winks to everyone below.

Girls wearing red, white and blue hats barge past me, laughing.

"Why so serious?" one of them calls out. "It's over!" She leans over, looking like she's about to kiss my cheek, but her friend pulls her away, giggling.

In front of me, a boy and girl link arms. She kicks her legs up and he sings, noisily and out of tune, "Knees up Mother Brown!" – I've no idea who Mother Brown is, but other people must have heard of her, because the crowds join in.

Buckingham Palace isn't far from here; I could easily walk. The King, Queen and maybe Churchill too will probably come out to make a speech, but with so many people everywhere, I might not get there.

The air is bright and buzzy, but I'm tired. King George isn't my king, anyway. When the princesses think of home, do they imagine broken glass and smeared paint?

Walking to the Tube station, the smiling, laughing people are all headed in the opposite direction, and it's almost as if they carry away the fizzy fun feelings that had sizzled through me earlier.

Stepping on to the Tube carriage, apart from a snoring old man with his cap pulled down low and a beer bottle rolling down the aisle, it's quiet.

Sadness washes over me. Who is this victory really for? Mama and Papa might be dead. Even if, by a miracle, they're safe, will we ever be together again?

The sky is dusky pink as I walk up to the front gate. Streamers litter the road.

When the Cohens are asleep, I sit at my desk and take out a piece of writing paper.

Dear Mama and Papa, I begin. A tear splashes on to the paper and I wipe it away, smearing the ink. I no longer remember how to write German.

How can I ever go home if the language of my country is lost to me?

English will have to do... for now.

FACT FILE

KINDERTRANSPORT

•••

'Kindertransport', also known as the Refugee Children's Movement, was the operation that rescued many thousands of children from the dangers of Nazi Germany before the Second World War began. Almost 10,000 children came to Britain by train and boat from Germany, Poland, Czechoslovakia, as it was then known, and Austria.

The first 196 children arrived in Britain on 2 December 1938. They had been rescued from an orphanage burned down by the Nazis during Kristallnacht.

The Kindertransport children lived with families all over the UK for the duration of the war. After the war, most of these child refugees stayed in Britain, with some emigrating to Australia, the US and Israel. Most never saw their parents again.

KINDERTRANSPORT IN NUMBERS

Children on the first Kindertransport: 196
Total children rescued: nearly 10,000
Age of children rescued: 17 and under
Arrival dates: approximately
December 1938 to September 1939

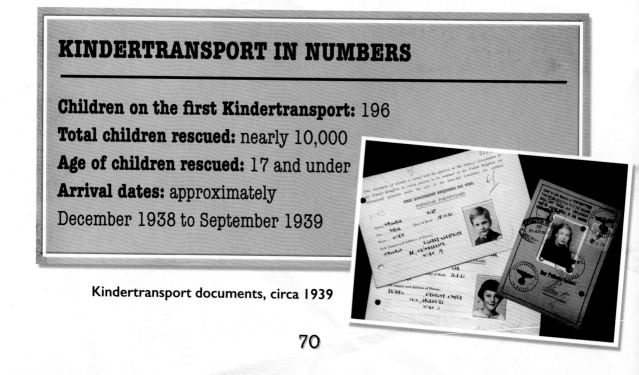

Kindertransport documents, circa 1939

'Kindertransport – The Arrival' statue, Hope Square, Liverpool Street Station, London

KRISTALLNACHT – NIGHT OF BROKEN GLASS

During the two days and nights of 9 and 10 November 1938, Nazi forces and their supporters attacked Jewish people, synagogues, homes and businesses throughout Germany. Many buildings were burned to the ground and many innocent Jewish people were arrested, injured or killed.

This pogrom – an organized attack on a group of people – was given the name 'Kristallnacht', or 'Night of Broken Glass', because the streets were littered with shards of glass from the devastating events. After Kristallnacht, life for Jewish people in Germany became more and more unbearable.

A synagogue burning during Kristallnacht

OSKAR SCHINDLER

As well as the Kindertransport movement to protect refugee children, there were individuals who worked to protect Jewish people from Nazi hate.

Oskar Schindler was a German businessman and member of the Nazi Party who owned factories in Poland. During the Second World War he rescued an estimated 1,000 people from being sent to the largest concentration camp, Auschwitz, by employing them in a factory. He insisted to the Nazi officials that his Jewish workers were essential to the German war effort, and kept them as safe from harm as possible.

Oskar Schindler in Argentina after the Second World War

AN END TO KILLING

PAWEL ADAMSKI
POLISH PARTISAN, AGED 25

BY TONY BRADMAN

Pawel Adamski heard the sound of gunfire as they reached the edge of the woods. He raised his arm, signalling to those behind him to take cover. They silently obeyed, fifty hardened rebel fighters hunkering down in the shadows, weapons ready.

"We'd better take a look," Pawel said quietly. "Jerzy, Katerina, with me."

The three of them crept onto the road beyond and turned right, making for the gunfire. It was coming from a village a hundred metres further along. A column of smoke rose above the buildings, and as they got closer they heard shouting.

"They're speaking German," muttered Jerzy with a frown. He gripped his machine gun more tightly. "I reckon it might be a trap..."

"I don't think so," said Katerina. "The person who's doing all the shouting has got a Czech accent, and he's saying that the war is over."

"Well, we know he's right about that, don't we?" said Pawel. They had heard on the radio last night – 7 May – that the Germans had surrendered. "Jerzy, go back and fetch the others. Come on then, Katerina. Let's go and see what's happening."

Jerzy ran back to the forest, and Katerina strode towards the village, her machine gun at the ready. Pawel smiled. He and Jerzy and Katerina had been together for such a long time, and he knew he could rely on them. They had seen so much in all the years of death and destruction. It was so hard to believe it was all coming to an end. Sometimes Pawel could barely remember what life had been like before...

Pawel had been born in Lwów, Eastern Poland, and had been called up in 1939 to fight the Nazi invaders. But the Germans had been unstoppable, and then their ancient enemies, the Soviet Union, had stabbed Poland in the back. They had invaded from the east, and within a few weeks it was all over: Poland was conquered. Pawel had fled with the remnants of the Polish army across the border into Hungary.

The worst thing had been losing contact with his family – his parents and his little brother Marek. Pawel had tried everything he could to find out if they were all right, but it was no use. So he decided to carry on the struggle against the Germans, and over the next few years he fought in many places. Eventually he became the leader of a Yugoslav secret armed group – the Partisans – that included Serbs, Slovaks and Poles.

For a long time the Germans had seemed invincible. Then the tide of war turned and they started to lose. The Soviet Union had swapped sides after the Germans had invaded them as well. Pawel would never forgive them for their betrayal of Poland, but by 1944 the Soviet Red Army was sweeping the Germans out of Eastern Europe. Then D-Day happened, and soon they were being swept out of the West too.

By the spring of 1945 everyone could see the end was near, but the Germans wouldn't give up. Pawel thought that was because they had done such evil things and knew they would be punished for them – the Partisans knew all about the death camps in Poland. Pawel often thought of his parents and Marek. Pawel had been nineteen at the beginning of the war and Marek nine, so he'd be fifteen now, if he was still alive...

Pawel and Katerina reached the edge of the village and stopped beside a small cottage. They peered round the wall and Pawel saw a dozen Partisans in the village square, their uniforms a wild mixture, just like those of Pawel's unit. Some wore old Czech or Polish army jackets and helmets, but many had Red Army gear or stolen German battledress. They were all armed with rifles or machine guns.

The Partisans had taken cover in doorways and behind a German lorry that had been badly shot up. They were shooting at the large tavern on the far side of the square. Bullets thwacked into the brickwork, and the roof was on fire. Pawel could see dark figures behind the windows – German soldiers in their instantly recognizable 'coal-scuttle' helmets.

They were trying to fire back, but were clearly losing.

Suddenly the door of the tavern opened and somebody stuck out a broom handle with a white sheet tied to it. The leader of the Czech Partisans yelled, "Cease fire!" in Czech, and the Partisans lowered their guns. "Right, throw out your weapons!" the leader shouted, in German this time. The Germans inside quickly did as they were ordered, rifles and machine guns clattering on the cobbles of the square.

Then they emerged, five soldiers in scruffy, dirty uniforms. One had a blood-soaked bandage round his head and was being supported by two comrades. Pawel saw that another was very young. He knew the Germans had lost so many soldiers that they had begun to call up boys. This lad was no more than fourteen, and looked terrified. There was something about him that reminded Pawel of Marek, too.

Pawel moved forward into the square, Katerina following. The Partisans turned to point their weapons at them, but soon realized they were rebel fighters, too.

"What are you going to do with them?" Pawel asked the leader of the Czech Partisans. He had learned Czech and now spoke it almost as well as Polish.

"What do you think?" said the leader, grinning. "We're going to shoot them."

Pawel stared at him. Jerzy appeared at Pawel's side, and he heard the rest of the unit fanning out behind them. The Czech Partisans began to look very uneasy.

"I don't think so," Pawel said quietly. "If the war is over, then there must be an end to killing. We'll take them prisoner, then work out what to do with them later."

There was silence in the square for a moment. Then the leader shrugged.

"Fair enough," he said. "I hadn't thought of it that way, but you're right…"

Pawel glanced at the young German soldier. Their eyes met, and Pawel thought again of Marek and his parents. Perhaps they were thinking of him, too.

That night, all the Partisans celebrated, and the next day they went their separate ways. Pawel, Jerzy and Katerina went west, and met American soldiers who took their weapons and sent them to a camp for 'displaced persons' in Germany, near Frankfurt. Pawel's hatred for the Germans began to drain away when he saw how badly the city had been bombed. Barely a building had been left standing.

Months went by and the camp slowly emptied as people began to go home. Those from the West went back to their own countries, but that just wasn't possible for those from most of Eastern Europe, especially the Poles. The Soviet Union had occupied Poland and put the eastern part – including Lwów – into the Ukraine, a republic of the Soviet Union. So, Pawel didn't have a home country he could go back to.

Eventually, Pawel was offered the chance to live in England – and he took it. Jerzy and Katerina went with him, to yet another camp, but they all soon moved on – although they always kept in touch. Pawel never went back to Poland and he never did find out what had happened to his parents or his little brother Marek. But he got married and had children of his own and had a long and good life in his new homeland.

And he often thought of the young German he had saved on VE Day, 8 May 1945.

THE POLISH RESISTANCE

Germany and the Soviet Union invaded Poland in September 1939, but the Polish people did not give up easily. The Polish resistance movement, led by the Home Army, was loyal to the Polish government who were forced to rule from France and Great Britain.

The Home Army were hugely outnumbered but remained very active. They produced their own weapons, destroyed Nazi railway engines, blew up three bridges and set fire to over 230 German transport lorries.

Polish armed forces that had escaped the country when Germany invaded fought alongside the Allies in battles such as the Siege of Tobruk (see page 19).

THE WARSAW UPRISING

The uprising was the Polish Home Army's attempt to free Warsaw from Nazi Germany.

Length: 63 days, August to October 1944
Deaths: 16,000 resistance members and over 150,000 civilians
Destruction: around 35 per cent of the city

Above: soldiers of the Polish Home Army during the Warsaw Uprising, 5 August 1944. The men are dressed in stolen German uniforms and armed with confiscated German weapons.

Right: the Polish Home Army Cross, awarded post-war to Polish resistance members, civilians and Allied air crews involved in the Warsaw Uprising – including to Flight Sergeant Bill James, seen second left in the picture on page 83.

THE WARSAW AIRLIFTS

The tide of war had changed in 1944 – German troops were being driven back from Russia through Poland. When the Soviet armies reached Warsaw, the Polish government-in-exile ordered an uprising. They wanted to take back control of their city before the Soviet Union could grab power.

Churchill decided that Great Britain had a duty to help their ally, Poland. He ordered supply drops to take place in Warsaw, despite having been told that these flights would be very dangerous. RAF squadrons 148 (Special Duties) and 178 were given orders to take part in the 1,750-mile (2,800-km) round trips. These night flights from Brindisi in Italy to Warsaw, over Yugoslavia, Hungary, Poland and Czechoslovakia, were the longest single missions undertaken by RAF Bomber Command.

Halifax planes were specially adapted for this job. Flight Sergeant Bill James, a rear gunner for Squadron 148 (seen second from left in the picture on page 83) remembered flying to such a low level that he could see down chimneys as they approached their targets. He saw Germans on one side of Warsaw, and Soviets on the other. His logbook records him firing on both Soviet and German night fighters.

These Polish missions show that British Bomber Command did many other things than bombing. However, it was not enough to keep the Nazis away and Warsaw fell on 2 October 1944. Poland would not be free again until the end of the communist-led government in the early 1990s.

Right: a Handley Page Halifax Mark II of Squadron 148 (SD) at Brindisi, Italy, before taking off on a supply-dropping mission

An all-Welsh crew of RAF Squadron 148 (SD), sitting on the tail of their Halifax plane in Tocra, Libya, October 1943

WE'LL MEET AGAIN

MARY MARTIN
ATS DESPATCH RIDER, AGED 24

BY EMILY HIBBS

"**W**atch out!" I cried, squeezing the brakes as hard as I could.

Eva jumped out of the way of my motorcycle just in time, toppling over into the mud with a squelch. I skidded to a halt, swung off the bike and rushed over to help her up.

"Why did you run out in front of me?" I asked, hefting Eva on to her feet. "You could have been flattened!"

Far from looking put out, Eva's eyes were alight with excitement.

"Sorry," she said, not sounding sorry in the slightest. "But we've just heard – we've won! It's over, Mary. At least, almost over. It won't be long until the Japanese throw in the towel."

She crushed me into a hug. Eva hardly came up to my chin, and I got a sharp jab in the cheek from the ATS badge attached to her hat.

"Really?" I asked, as soon as she released me.

"Truly," Eva said breathlessly. "Churchill made the announcement at three o'clock. The Germans have surrendered. I've been haunting the yard waiting for you to come back since."

I pulled off my helmet and began to lug my motorcycle towards the shed. My body ached from the bumpy journey home. Many of the roads between Sunderland and the base at Goosepool were still littered with debris from the raids, and navigating the potholes in the dark could be perilous for a despatch rider on two wheels. Once the bike was safely stowed, we turned back towards the hostel.

"Aren't you excited?" Eva asked.

"Of course," I replied, forcing my mouth into a smile. "Where's Betty?"

"Probably in our room curling her—"

"Girls!"

Eva and I froze at the booming voice of our officer. We snapped to attention as she approached.

"The war may be over, but that is no reason to let the standards of the Auxiliary Territorial Service slip. Mary, I could forgive your appearance as I assume you've just got back from a delivery, but Eva, there is no excuse for the state of your uniform!"

With me muttering apologies and Eva stifling giggles, we headed up to our dorm.

"You two look ghastly," Betty said, glancing up as we came into the room. She was perched on the edge of her bed, twisting dinky curlers into her hair. Eva stuck out her tongue. The three of us had bunked together since our driver training four years ago. The pair of them were as different as coal and custard – Betty a society girl from London and Eva a farmer's daughter from Bristol – but we had found a way to muddle along together.

Women in the ATS could take on all sorts of jobs, from cooks to clerks, ammunition inspectors to searchlight operators – anything that freed up the men for the fighting – but all three of us had known we wanted to be drivers from the outset. Eva and I could already handle a vehicle; she'd learned to drive in her father's tractor, and I in my father's furniture delivery truck. Betty hadn't a clue about driving, but she wanted to join the transport division because Princess Elizabeth had.

My mother had begged me to train as a nurse rather than join the ATS. She'd been a nurse in Kingston, Jamaica, before she moved to Sunderland after the First World War. I'd seen her struggle to find employment in this country and didn't want to face the daily prejudice she still suffered. Not that driving for the ATS was easy. As an ambulance driver, I'd attended countless raids. The worst came when, in May 1943, many people were killed at the Sunderland shipyards in a single attack. Reg had held me for hours afterwards. I couldn't stop shaking, trying to get the awful scene out of my head.

"There's a mug of tea for you there. It might still be warm," Betty told me as I changed into my off-duty uniform – a khaki skirt and pressed shirt. "I don't know how I'm going to get my hair finished before lights out."

"You could always wear it straight," suggested Eva. "Like Hitler."

Betty threw a curler at her with a shriek.

A few hours later, the three of us slipped into our beds. Betty and Eva whispered about their plans to go into Sunderland for the celebrations the next day until, eventually, they dropped off. Once I was sure they were asleep, I reached under my pillow and pulled out the letter I had received over a year before. It was too dark to read it, but I knew the note by heart.

ON BEHALF OF THE ROYAL AIR FORCE, I REGRET TO INFORM YOU THAT YOUR HUSBAND, FLIGHT LIEUTENANT REGINALD MARTIN, HAS BEEN KILLED AS A RESULT OF AIR OPERATIONS OVER SICILY. I EXTEND TO YOU MY SINCERE SYMPATHY ON YOUR GREAT LOSS.

We'd barely been married a year when it happened. He'd lived on the base, too, and we'd met at one of the weekly dances held in the mess hall. Some of the other airmen had given me a wide berth, and a couple of the American GIs even made awful comments under their breath – I knew they forced their black soldiers to live, eat and work separately, and were probably horrified to learn that a mixed-race woman was sharing a dorm with two white girls. But Reg had come right over and asked if I wanted to dance. We'd whirled around the floor all night, chatting and laughing like we were the only two people in the room. Each time he was back on leave, Reg and I would go to the pictures or stroll around the base. When he got down on one knee, it was easy to say yes. It was a proper wartime wedding, with both of us in uniform.

We weren't married long, but it was wonderful. When the note came informing me of his death, my world fell apart. I would never again breathe in the warm smell of his overcoat, or hear him whistle 'We'll Meet Again', his favourite wartime tune. We would never make plans to visit my mother's hometown in Jamaica. It was those little absences that added up to one great big loss.

After the letter, I couldn't face getting back into an ambulance and seeing any more death. I'd retrained as a despatch rider, trading four wheels for two, and delivering messages across the county. It was the ATS that had pulled me out of the darkness, really. It had given me a reason to get up each day, put on my uniform and do something useful. But now the war was over. Once the men came home, would we still be needed? I lay uneasily in the darkness, worrying. I had already lost Reg – was I about to lose my job and my friends, too?

BOOM!

I leaped out of bed. Eva flung off her blanket and Betty sat bolt upright, staring wildly around the room looking for the source of the almighty crash.

"Was that a bomb?" Betty asked.

"Surely not!" said Eva. It had been months and months since we'd had an air raid: besides, the war was supposed to be over.

I pulled on my coat and boots and headed out into the yard. The base was in a ruckus with RAF men swarming around in the dark.

"What happened?" I asked a flight officer rushing past me, heading back towards the girls' hostel.

"A few of the men got carried away with the celebrations and let off some shells from a vessel anchored on the River Wear," he said, rolling his eyes.

I followed him back up the steps into the hostel and through to another dormitory. Sure enough, a 20mm Oerlikon shell had struck the ceiling, leaving a gaping hole. The bed beneath was dusted in plaster and three ATS girls huddled together in their nightclothes, looking shaken. It seemed the drama of the war wasn't quite over yet!

The following weeks slipped by in a haze of celebrations. Although I tried to join in, I often felt like I was floating above it all. Betty and Eva returned to London and Bristol. It was hard to say goodbye, but we swore we'd write to each other every week. I stayed on at the base, granted 'extended service' terms to continue working as a despatch rider. There were still messages to deliver, after all, and I was determined to stay in uniform for as long as I could.

I was putting my motorcycle away one July afternoon, the yard dusty in the sunlight, when a shadow fell across the floor of the shed. I turned around and saw an impossible sight.

I had to grip my bike to stop me from falling.

Reg stood in the doorway; thin, pale and with shadows like bruises beneath his eyes. I reached out a hand to grip his arm, to make sure he was real.

"Mary," he said. And with that one word, the whole war came tumbling down around us.

Reg explained he had survived the crash, bailed out and been captured by the enemy. He'd spent the time since in a prisoner-of-war camp in Bavaria, Germany, with no way of getting word to me.

He was horrified to discover I had received a telegram telling me of his death, and even more horrified to learn I had slept with it under my pillow for all this time.

We knew we were lucky – there were so many that hadn't come home. As we walked arm in arm across the base, the future suddenly didn't seem quite so daunting. Whatever hardships the next few years would bring, we could face them together.

FACT FILE

THE AUXILIARY TERRITORIAL SERVICE (ATS)

The ATS was the women's branch of the British Army during the Second World War. The equivalent service in the First World War had been called the Women's Army Auxiliary Corps (WAAC) – but the ATS had many more varied roles available.

Women were not allowed to fight or fire guns, but still served in most theatres of war. **ATS roles included:**

- cook
- baker
- clerk
- storekeeper
- telephonist
- car mechanic
- driver
- despatch rider
- mess orderly
- postal worker
- ammunition inspector
- military police
- searchlight operator
- translator
- radar operator

They can't get on without us

JOIN ME IN THE NEW ATS
A VITAL BRANCH

THE ATS IN NUMBERS

Established: September 1938

Disbanded: 1949 – succeeded by the WRAC (Women's Royal Army Corps)

Size: over 200,000 at its height, including 2,000 from across the Commonwealth

Age of recruits: 18 to 50 years

ATS POWs: 20

ATS wounded: 302

Killed in action: 335

Left: HRH Princess Elizabeth in her ATS uniform, April 1945

Below: members of the West Indian ATS at a garden party

THE BRITISH EMPIRE
AND COMMONWEALTH

• •

When war broke out in 1939, Great Britain still ruled over approximately 25 per cent of the world's population – this was called the British Commonwealth of Nations, but still informally known as the British Empire.

The British directly or partly ruled over India and the West Indies, as well as colonies in the Far East and Africa. The self-ruled countries of Australia, New Zealand, South Africa and Canada were also part of the Commonwealth.

On VE Day, King George VI said of this united front that had successfully defeated the Axis powers:

"The Queen and I know the ordeals which you have endured throughout the Commonwealth and Empire. We are proud to have shared some of these ordeals with you, and we know also that together we shall all face the future with stern resolve."

THE EMPIRE'S MEN

Total in military service:
- 5 million from the British Isles
- 1,440,500 from India
- 629,000 from Canada
- 413,000 from Australia
- 136,000 from South Africa
- 128,500 from New Zealand
- more than 134,000 from other colonies.

A British propaganda poster from 1939 showing: a West African soldier in slouch hat; an Indian soldier wearing a turban; a British soldier in pith helmet; a New Zealand soldier in 'lemon squeezer' slouch hat; an airman of the Royal Canadian Air Force in blue uniform; an Australian soldier in slouch hat; and a sailor of the Royal Navy in dark blue naval uniform.

A WORLD AWAY FROM SANITARY STREET

JILL PARFITT
LAND GIRL, AGED 22

BY LEILA RASHEED

Well, honey, I am just so proud of you. I can hardly believe you're going all the way to old England to study, to Manchester where I was born! And of course, you want to hear all about it, and what it was like in the war for me, your Great-Grandma Jill. Goodness, I'll do my best. It was such a long time ago, but I can still remember where we used to live…

If I'm honest, sweetie, Sanitary Street never felt like home. I know we were lucky to live there, but I never got used to the way all the houses looked the same, marching away over the hills, like a lot of grey bullets pumped out of a Sten machine gun. And it was a squeeze – me, Mam, Dad and two loud, stinky boys all sharing three bedrooms. Then, in 1940, Albert and Jack got called up to join the army. I hugged them both goodbye.

"Look after Mam and Dad," said Jack. He was always the joker, but when I waved them off from the front door, his face looked as white as my handkerchief. I tried not to cry. There was no point in crying. They weren't the only ones to go. The war was taking all our boys and men. Now the house felt empty, without big voices and daft jokes to fill it.

"You could get a job in a factory, Jill," my mam said to me, a few weeks later. "There's lots of war work now. You can't do nothing."

I agreed. But I wasn't going to work in a factory. It was what Mam had done, and so she liked the idea, but I knew I couldn't bear being inside all day.

"I want to join the Women's Land Army," I told my parents.

"Why? When there's perfectly good work right here near us?" Mam protested.

It was the Manchester Blitz that changed her mind. Thank heavens we didn't get hit, but afterwards, Mam thought I would be safer out of the city. So, in 1941 I signed up as a Land Girl.

I was sent to a farm in Hertfordshire. I'll never forget my first day. Sitting in the back of a truck jolting up the rutted farm track, frozen stiff, with cabbages rolling around me. It wasn't glamorous! But the dawn light was silver, and the air didn't smell of coal.

Mind you, my first cow was a shock. Her name was Betty.

I remember standing there with the milk pail in one hand and the stool in the other, gaping at her. I think they ought to warn kids about cows in school. No one tells you they're so big, or that some of them are just mean. Betty gave me a hard stare. She could tell I was new, I'm sure.

"Now you and me, Betty, we're going to be friends," I told her. I sat down, and tried to milk her. Nothing doing. The farmer must have thought I was a real idiot, but he helped me and showed me what to do. Betty was good as gold until the farmer went away. Then she trod in the full pail and spilled it. And she thwacked me in the eye with her tail when I tried to pick it up again.

"Don't you know there's a war on?" was all I could think to say to her. You had to laugh or you'd cry, sometimes.

By 1943, I felt as if the war had started at Creation and would keep going on till Judgement Day. I wrote to my parents and they wrote back telling me who had had *that* letter. Not us, yet, thank God. In two years I'd seen Albert twice and Jack once. They were so much more grown up now, and it hurt my heart that Jack didn't make the jokes he used to.

As time went on, I made friends with some of the other Land Girls. There was an airbase nearby, so there were always handsome young airmen who would come to the dances in the village. I had to leave the dances early to get back to the farm, so I was really excited when I found out I was going to be moved to live in a hostel in the village, with the other Land Girls.

I bunked with a tall, dark-haired girl called Margot, with a voice like Princess Elizabeth's. She said hello coldly, and then ignored me. I decided she was a snob.

The first night I was lying in bed when I heard Margot sobbing quietly. "What's up?" I asked.

I might have guessed it: she'd had a letter. One of those letters. Her twin brother had been the gunner in a plane shot down over the North Sea.

I sat up with her the whole night. I didn't want to feel guilty, but I did – I still had two brothers.

I tried to explain but Margot shut me up fast: "Don't you dare wish your brothers dead." I couldn't say anything to that, but afterwards we were friends.

I used to ride around to other farms in the area on a bicycle, meeting new people and milking new cows. Two years in and I could cope with any cow now. The bicycle was another matter. It had a way of trying to throw you off into the mud. I named it Betty after my least favourite cow.

One day I was struggling with Betty down the village high street in the rain, loaded up with packages. I may have been using language my mother wouldn't have liked to hear, when I heard a strange voice.

"Can I help you there, ma'am?"

I looked up, and saw twinkling blue eyes. Then I saw the uniform.

"Oh, the Americans have arrived!" I exclaimed without thinking. We'd heard they were coming to the airbase – there had been lots of gossip and excitement.

"We sure have," he said with a grin. "Special bicycle repair corps."

His name was Charles Olsen, but before I knew it I was calling him Charlie. He was from Wisconsin, a place I'd never heard of, but the way he talked about it made it sound wonderful: big and free. We saw each other whenever we could.

"Just think," said Margot, "if it hadn't been for the war you two would never have met at all!"

I switched off the radio and couldn't think what to say. 8 May 1945 – the war was over and we'd won. It was incredible!

"What shall we do?" said Margot. "We can't just sit in the hostel, as if it was an ordinary day!"

"Let's go to London!" I said. It was a mad idea but there would never be another day like this in my life. I didn't want to look back and say I missed it all.

We cycled to the station, the church bells ringing all around us as we spun through the village. All through the war, we'd had to keep a stiff upper lip. Now people were laughing, crying and hugging complete strangers.

"I feel like a bottle of champagne, all bubbly!" Margot said, and though I'd never tasted champagne I knew what she meant. I felt as if everyone had been pent up for years and years and now we were finally getting the cork pulled out. The closer and closer we got to London, the more excited I felt, and when we finally burst out of the train at St Pancras station, we were so glad we'd come.

The first thing we did was get a bus to St Paul's – luckily Margot knew where she was going. We said a prayer, for her brother and my Uncle Ted who'd been killed the year before. It was a solemn moment as we thought about everyone who had given their lives to keep us safe.

We walked down towards Trafalgar Square. There were crowds gathering. Some people were wildly happy and some were just wandering around as if they weren't sure what to do with themselves. It was a hot day, so we stopped in a pub. The barman saw our Land Girl coats, and shouted, "On the house for these ladies, they've been doing their bit." I felt so proud when everyone looked at us and cheered.

Then in Trafalgar Square everyone was dancing in the fountains and we were feeling giddy after the drink, so we joined in. A sailor grabbed me and whirled me around to the music, and even though his breath smelled of beer I went with it, laughing and squealing. Then, of course, splash we went down in the fountain! But it was marvellous, no one cared.

We stayed in London till evening. We saw the King and Queen on the balcony at Buckingham Palace, though we missed Winston Churchill's speech. When it got dark, bonfires were lit all down The Mall and it felt as good as Bonfire Night when I was a child.

We didn't get back to the hostel until past midnight. My feet were aching and I was asleep as I walked, leaning on Margot. But as we went up towards the door, I could see there was someone sitting on the front step.

"Who's that?" said Margot.

"It's Charlie!" I said, astonished. "What are you doing here at this time of night?"

"Waiting for you to get back so I can ask you to marry me, Jill!" he said – and I realized he was holding a ring. So, what did I do? Hug him? Kiss him? Well, no. I burst into tears!

It wasn't that I didn't want to marry him. I did, more than anything. But I knew what it would mean. All over the world, other people were coming home from the war to their families. I would be going far away from my family, to find a new home over the sea.

So that's how your Great-Grandma Jill came to be here, on Whitegates Farm, Wisconsin, USA, a world away from Sanitary Street. Charlie and I married soon after the war so I only got to see Mam and Dad and Albert a few more times before we crossed the pond. Jack moved over to the USA a few years after me, though he lives in New York.

I love the big skies out here and I don't regret a thing. But I'm glad you're going to study in Manchester, sweetie. You'll see the house on Sanitary Street, though I hear they've changed the name now. Maybe you'll feel at home there, who knows? Sometimes you have to travel the world to find the perfect place to call home.

FACT FILE

WOMEN AT WORK

· ·

Before the war, women who married usually gave up their jobs to work within the home. This all changed during the Second World War. With many working-age men away fighting, women had to step in and take on their jobs to keep the country running.

From 1941, women aged between eighteen and sixty were called up to register for war work. They had the choice of joining the armed forces, the Women's Land Army or working in factories. At the height of the war more than seven million women were at work.

Women in the Land Army did back-breaking work on farms, while in the factories women made everything from planes and bombs to parachutes. The Women's Timber Corps (around 6,000 women known as 'Lumber Jills') felled trees, measured logs and loaded them onto trucks.

In the armed forces, women operated searchlights and radar while others worked as codebreakers. A few even worked behind enemy lines as secret agents.

For a healthy, happy job

Join the WOMEN'S LAND ARMY

APPLY TO NEAREST W.L.A. COUNTY OFFICE OR TO W.L.A HEADQUARTERS 6 CHESHAM PLACE LONDON S.W.1

Right: a member of the Women's Timber Corps stripping the bark from a tree to be used as a telegraph pole

Main picture: Mrs Cheatle of Sheffield at a munitions factory in Yorkshire

THE MANCHESTER BLITZ

London wasn't the only city in the UK to be hit by the Blitz. On 23 December 1940, the industrial city of Manchester was hit by two attacks – this was also known as the Christmas Blitz. The city was targeted because it housed industries such as the A. V. Roe aircraft factory building Manchester and Lancaster bombers.

Both of Manchester's main train stations as well as Manchester United's football ground, Old Trafford, were badly hit during the raids.

THE MANCHESTER BLITZ IN NUMBERS

Civilians killed: estimated 684
Civilians injured: approximately 2,000
Bombs dropped (tons): 467

Right: firemen directing hoses on burning buildings in Manchester

Far right: buildings burning in Manchester after a German air raid on the night of 23 December 1940

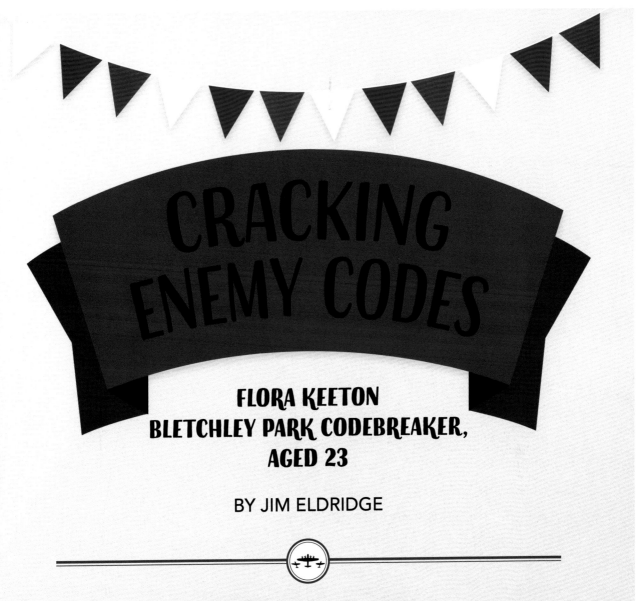

CRACKING ENEMY CODES

FLORA KEETON
BLETCHLEY PARK CODEBREAKER,
AGED 23

BY JIM ELDRIDGE

8 MAY 1945, VE DAY

*L*ondon's Whitehall is the perfect place to celebrate, thought Flora. No, she corrected herself; Buckingham Palace would have been the perfect place.

But when she and her friends had reached London from Bletchley Park and tried to get to the palace, the crowd had been so vast they had hardly been able to get into The Mall; it would have been impossible to see the King and Queen when they came out on to the balcony with Princesses Elizabeth and Margaret.

Instead, Flora and her friend Mavis had decided to go to Whitehall where the prime minister, Winston Churchill, was due to address the crowds from a balcony at the Ministry of Health, but on their way along Whitehall Flora and Mavis had become separated. It was hardly surprising: it wasn't just the size of the crowd but the fact that it kept moving: soldiers, sailors and airmen home on leave would grab a woman and start dancing with her, or an impromptu conga dance would break out, with revellers joining a long line of people dancing along the street, snaking through the crowds, only to break up and rush back to the Ministry of Health and joyfully chant, "We want Winnie!" It was a mass outburst of relief after almost six long years of war, years of terror from bombing, of losing loved family members at home or serving overseas.

Flora had been sixteen when the war began. From her parents' house in Fulham, southwest London, she'd seen the daily aerial combats of the Battle of Britain and watched London burning at night during the Blitz. She'd felt the loss when her two older brothers, twins Tom and Barry, had been called up and gone abroad to fight, first in North Africa, and then to Italy. The last message her parents had had from them was to say they were now in Germany. At least they were alive.

Flora's own contribution to the war effort had to be kept secret, even now that the war in Europe was over. When she'd turned eighteen in 1941 she'd applied to join the ATS, but had ended up as a codebreaker in Hut 8 at Bletchley Park. It was her love of puzzles, especially cryptic crosswords, which had led to it. Apparently the people who ran Bletchley Park – the secret centre set up to crack enemy codes – checked everyone applying to join the services to sort out those who showed ability at unscrambling puzzles. As a result, Bletchley Park was staffed by chess grandmasters, professors of mathematics, and those who could complete the *Daily Telegraph* crossword in less than twelve minutes. They were looking for more than quick thinkers; they were looking for those who spotted recognizable patterns in jumbles of words and numbers, and Flora had been able to do that from a very early age. She'd realized when she'd been at school that this made her different from most of the other children, that in some way she was 'odd'.

At Bletchley Park, she was just one of many; everyone there could be defined as 'odd'. And none odder than Alan Turing, the man who'd been in charge of Hut 8 when she first joined the team. The fact that he was a mathematical genius was generally acknowledged, but it was his appearance that marked him out. His clothes were shabby and creased, his trousers held up by a length of string around his waist. When he was excited, which was often, his stammer became so pronounced that he couldn't get out what he wanted to say, so he communicated in numbers, and so skilfully that people knew what he meant. But then, he was talking to the like-minded, those who saw in patterns. Not that Flora ever considered herself on the same level as Turing, or any of the other top-level codebreakers.

Hut 8 caught messages sent from the German navy. Other huts dealt with coded messages from the German army and air force.

The process began with team members listening in to wireless traffic between German commanders and their outposts, including U-boats, and transcribing the messages, which were in German and in the top-secret Enigma code. These were passed to Flora and her colleagues, most of them also women, to identify patterns in the jumble of letters the radio interceptors picked up, and to pass anything promising on to more senior officers. They in turn ran it through the Bombe, a type of computer constructed with lots of valves, working at speeds faster than any human in an effort to break the code. The problem with cracking the Enigma code was not that they had to examine thousands of messages in code every day, nor that the sending machine used an encryption system that had trillions of possible combinations, but that the key code was changed constantly. So, it may have been broken once, but every time the key code was changed they had to start all over again. And each time, the longer it took to crack the code, the more Allied ships were in danger of being sunk by German U-boats, and the precious cargos many were bringing to Britain would disappear beneath the waves, forcing Britain towards starvation, and possible surrender.

It had been Turing who'd come up with the solution: for the code-breakers to look for short repeated standard phrases in the transcripts, things like "Heil Hitler" or "Weather for the night" and "Nothing to report". Translate and crack those, and the trickier messages would follow. It worked, and from then on Bletchley would continue to win the War of the Codes.

Flora's only regret was that their work was so secret they weren't allowed to tell anyone about it, not even close family. As far as the outside world was concerned, Bletchley Park was either an office, or – as some rumours had it – a rest centre for injured young men sent home from the war.

"No one must ever know what goes on here," her boss had told her when she began work there. "No one. Not your family, or your husband or children if you should marry. No one." As Flora looked about her at the rejoicing crowds, she felt sad that none of them would ever know how much the people at Bletchley had done to help the Allies win the war. It was her victory just as much as the armed forces' and everyone else in uniform. Hers and her colleagues'.

"Flora!" It was Mavis, pushing her way through the crowd towards Flora, her face flushed with excitement. "I've been dancing!"

"Who with?" asked Flora.

"Everyone!" Mavis laughed. "A sailor, a soldier, an airman, then a woman in engineering overalls! It was wonderful!"

The sudden shouts from the crowd of "He's here! He's here!" made them look up, as did everyone else, and there he was, Winston Churchill himself, on the balcony, his large trademark cigar between his fingers, waving at the crowd as they chanted, "Winnie! Winnie!" He held up his hand and the crowd quieted to hear him speak.

"This is your victory!" he declared.

"No!" roared back the crowd. "It's yours!"

They're all wrong, thought Flora. *It's ours. All of us. Everyone in uniform and out of it. At home and abroad. Wherever we are, this is our day.*

FACT FILE

THE BATTLE OF THE ATLANTIC

Non-military (merchant) ships brought much of the food and fuel Britain needed from other countries such as America and Australia on slow, dangerous journeys across the Atlantic Ocean. This made them targets for attack.

Merchant ships travelled in groups called convoys, with warships to guard them from Nazi planes and U-boats. These German submarines stalked convoys in terrifying groups called 'wolf packs'. They would wait until night fell, silently surface in the darkness and launch an attack.

The Allies fought back with long-range planes, as well as better radar, which could be used on both planes and ships. They also had improved sonar for detecting U-boats. A further breakthrough was made on 9 May 1941, when HMS *Bulldog* captured *U-110* off Greenland and sent men on board to see what they could find.

An anti-submarine depth charge explodes in the Atlantic beyond HMS *Starling*

THE BATTLE OF BRITAIN

In July 1940, the Nazis began bombing RAF airfields.

The plan was simple – without RAF planes to defend Britain, Hitler's troops could safely cross the Channel and invade. For the next two months, RAF Hurricanes and Spitfires took on the German Messerschmitts in fierce dogfights above the south coast of England.

Britain used a new technology called radar to alert RAF crews that enemy aircraft were approaching.

BATTLE OF BRITAIN IN NUMBERS

Code name: Operation Sealion
Planned invasion date: 15 September 1940
RAF planes: Supermarine Spitfire, Hawker Hurricane
Luftwaffe planes: Messerschmitt Bf 109, Messerschmitt Bf 110
Number of British planes (July 1940): 640
Number of Nazi planes (July 1940): 2,600
Average age of RAF pilots: 20
Life expectancy of a Spitfire pilot: four weeks
Countries who flew with the RAF: 15 (including Poland, Canada and New Zealand)

ENIGMA AND CODEBREAKING

Both sides used coded messages during the war. The Nazis had a powerful cypher machine called Enigma that they used to send messages. Messages were changed letter by letter by the machine to send them. To decode them, a second Enigma machine was needed, with the same settings. These settings changed every day and there were millions of combinations. So, the code was thought to be unbreakable.

Enigma Machine at the Imperial War Museum, London

But the Allies had a secret team of codebreakers working at Bletchley Park, the Government Code and Cypher School. Two of the team, Alan Turing and Gordon Welchman, built a machine called the Bombe. This, along with the Enigma machine found on U-boat *110*, helped them to break the code.

Alan Turing before the war at age sixteen

By 1945, there were many Bombe machines and millions of Nazi messages had been decoded. The amazing work of the wartime codebreakers is thought to have shortened the war by about two years.

Replica of a Bombe machine at Bletchley Park

SHIPMATES

GEORGE WANG
NAVAL RATING, AGED 24

BY TONY BRADMAN

"**Y**ou coming with the rest of us, George?" said my mate, Johnny.

I was in my hammock, taking it easy. I wasn't used to that – life on the Royal Navy destroyer HMS *Meynell* was usually pretty busy. But there hadn't been much to do since we'd docked at Chatham a few days before. Mind you, I reckoned the crew deserved a rest. In fact, after six terrible years of war, the whole country did.

"Where are you going, then?" I said, jumping out of the hammock.

"To London, of course, along with everyone else," he said, grinning.

"Come on, the lads are waiting for us dockside. If you don't hurry up we'll miss the train!"

I followed Johnny up on deck and down the gangway to the dock. Soon we were heading to the railway station with loads of our crewmates, everyone looking smart in their No. 1 uniforms. They were all so happy; it was 8 May, Victory in Europe Day. Adolf Hitler was dead, the Germans had finally surrendered, and we had come through it all. We had also been given twenty-four hours' shore leave.

I wasn't feeling quite so cheerful as Johnny, I have to admit. Oh, I was glad the war was over, and even more glad that we had won. The Nazis were evil and they had done some terrible things, so we had to beat them. But I'd been feeling uneasy, mostly because I wasn't sure what I was going to do now. It was impossible to see the future.

Chatham is a navy town, so the train was packed with sailors, although there were lots of civilians on it, too. We couldn't find any seats, which meant Johnny and I had to stand. I didn't mind. We were beside a window, and after months at sea it was good to see the green fields of Kent flying past as the train raced through them.

"Here, what's this?" somebody said. "A Chinaman in a sailor suit!"

A soldier was pointing at me and laughing with his mates. I sighed, and tried to take no notice. I'm half Chinese, born in Limehouse in London's East End to a Chinese dad and an English mum. My proper name is Wang Jian, but for some reason English people find that hard to say, so I go by 'George Wang' instead.

Chinese people have been living in Limehouse for a hundred years; mostly sailors from merchant ships who settled there. So you'd think the English would have got used to us by now. But they haven't, and when I was growing up, I got used to being called some terrible names – much worse than 'Chinaman' – though that doesn't mean I have to like it, even now.

"Hey, leave my pal alone!" said Johnny, glaring at the soldier. Johnny is small, not much more than five foot, but he grew up in a rough part of south London and he can be dead scary. "He's my mess-mate and I'll bet we've seen more action in this war than you! We were on Arctic convoy duty, and we did our bit on D-Day."

"Keep your hair on, shorty," said the soldier, smirking. "You're both heroes!"

"Leave it, Johnny," I said, pulling him away. "I'm fine, don't worry about it."

Johnny calmed down. But the soldier's words made me think, and I began to realize why I'd been feeling uneasy. Maybe this was what the future held for me – a life of being called ugly names, of being told that I didn't belong in England. Things had been different in the navy. I wasn't used to all that any more.

I was nineteen when the war began, but I didn't join up straightaway. I was far too busy helping my dad run our laundry business and my mum look after my three little sisters. Then the Blitz started, and the East End took a right hammering from the German air force, the Luftwaffe. None of us were hurt, but I realized then that I had to do my bit.

So I volunteered for the navy, because my dad had been a merchant seaman – a sailor working on ships that carried goods from country to country. I was assigned to HMS *Meynell* and we were on convoy duty, protecting the ships bringing food and war supplies from America or through the Arctic to Russia. We were at D-Day too, helping to get the troops ashore and bombarding the German defences.

As I stood on that train I thought of all the things I'd seen. Ships torpedoed and exploding, drowned sailors frozen solid in the Arctic, the night sky over Normandy lit up by warships firing their big guns. We'd been through all that together, my shipmates and I. I'd felt part of something, but that was about to come to an end…

"Blimey, just look at all these people!" said Johnny when we arrived in London. Thousands were pouring out of the trains and making their way outside.

We were swept into the street. Everyone was heading in the same direction and before long we were in Trafalgar Square. I had never seen so many happy people in one place. There were all sorts as well: British soldiers and sailors, Americans, Canadians, Free French, Poles, Norwegians, men, women, kids.

Those of us in uniform were very popular. People slapped us on the back and girls kissed us; we danced and sang and had the time of our lives. Later, Johnny and I ended up in the crowd at Buckingham Palace. The King and Queen came out on the balcony with the princesses and good old Winston Churchill, and we cheered them for ages. And for a while, deep in the heart of that crowd, I didn't feel uneasy any more.

I knew now that I had been part of something much bigger than the crew of HMS *Meynell*. Nobody could take that away from me, or any of us who were there.

"Right, come on, Johnny," I said at last. "I want you to meet my family."

It was time to go home.

MEYNELL

THE NAVY

In 1939, the Royal Navy had the largest fleet in the world. The ships fought to ensure goods and food could be transported and troops could land and fight the Axis powers.

It was very dangerous work, often in very rough seas, with attacks by enemy ships and planes as well as the danger of being torpedoed by a lurking Nazi U-boat.

German U-boat under attack, 1943

Aircraft carriers

Aircraft carriers allowed planes to be used out at sea. HMS *Ark Royal* could carry sixty Fairey Swordfish biplanes, with space-saving folding wings. You had to be made of stern stuff to pilot one of these planes – they took off using a giant catapult.

HMS *Ark Royal* before the war began

Submarines

Submarines were cramped and unpleasant. The crew slept in bunks wedged in all over the submarine – even the engine room. But that was nothing compared to the danger of being hit by a torpedo or depth charge.

Ships and submarines sent messages using Morse code. Each letter of the alphabet has a different combination of dots and dashes called 'dits' and 'dahs'.

D-DAY

By June 1944, the Allies had gathered enough forces to try to fight back against the Nazis in mainland Europe. The attack wouldn't be easy – they would have to move quickly to capture landing sites, and then move thousands of troops ashore with tanks and other equipment.

D-DAY INVASION OF NORMANDY

Code name: Operation Overlord

Supreme Commander: General Eisenhower

Leading the ground forces: General Montgomery

Date: 6 June 1944

Naval vessels: 7,000

Landing sites: five beaches on the Normandy coast

Paratroopers: 18,000

Troops landed day one: around 155,000

Troops landed by end of June: more than 845,000

DEMOBILIZATION

As the war came to an end, the servicemen and women – over 5 million across the UK armed services – started to come home. But it wasn't going to be an easy ride, as they needed to settle back into normal life, as well as find jobs and recover from the negative effects the war had had on their physical and mental health.

Each serviceperson, after completing their period of war service, went to a demobilization centre. There they swapped their uniform and personal kit for civilian-style clothing – also called a 'demob suit'. Men could choose a double-breasted pinstripe three-piece suit, or a single-breasted jacket with flannel trousers.

They could also choose a felt hat or flat cap. Women weren't given clothes but received clothing coupons instead.

Above: Mr Bill Krepper, late of the Pioneer Corps, leaves the demobilization clothing depot as a civilian, wearing his demob suit

Above: Sergeant H. Minnall is fitted with his civilian demob suit

JUST AN ORDINARY DAY

NELL HUTCHINSON
CHILD PRISONER OF WAR
IN THE FAR EAST, AGED 13

BY E.L. NORRY

It's *tenko*: roll call. A huge plane roars by overhead. On reflex, all of us in the line stare into the cloudless blue sky. An old woman next to me grins and her lips split. Licking them, she whispers, "That's a Skymaster, an American plane!"

"No talking!" the Japanese guard yells. "Stand up straight!"

She shuffles to lean on to her other hip, but grimaces, obviously in pain. The guard spits on to the ground, raising the butt of his rifle.

Although I've been in this Malay camp for four years, my heart still batters against my ribs and I bite my lip, trying to stop the tears, knowing what's coming.

The rifle butt smashes the old woman in the cheek. She collapses to her knees, whimpering. The rest of us remain silent, eyes to the ground. I focus on reflections from the sun bouncing off the dog tags around her neck.

When I first witnessed a guard strike a prisoner, I screamed. The guard charged over, yanked my hair and slammed my cheek into the dust. He told me I'd only survive by keeping my filthy mouth shut.

If only Father had just listened to Mother when she insisted that we leave Singapore!

It will be fine. The Japanese will be pushed back, he'd said, just before Christmas of '41.

Later, I made the mistake of looking a guard in the eye. My head was shaved as punishment. I wasted many tears over that. But, seeing others rife with lice, I realized they'd done me a favour.

We're punished for anything. I stood in the baking sun all day once, balancing a bucket of water on my head – just because half a rotten sweet potato was found in my pocket. I think that when the guards were boys, they probably pulled the legs off spiders.

What's that booming noise? I'd asked my ayah, the nanny who'd always been with me.

Artillery fire, she had said, holding me close.

Our camp is an old British army barracks with wooden huts. Any time I get too close to the bamboo barrier surrounding us, a soldier peers at me from up in his tower. I don't know why he's staring; it's far too high to climb. Some adults have been shot for trying.

Don't go outside to play! Mother had warned Bobby and I soon after New Year. *Stay with Ayah! It's not safe.*

After breakfast, it will be time to work. I'm too young to do the women's work of building barracks, so instead I clean wounds or set splints in the camp hospital. I pretend I'm Florence Nightingale doing my country a Great Service. Later, if the guards are in good spirits – which they should be, since they stole our latest Red Cross packages – I might be allowed to tend the vegetable patch. Most things have died but I like turning over the soil – it reminds me of Mother looking after her rose bushes.

We need to leave! Mother had cried, pleading with my father, day after day. But he refused to leave his desk, his office, his work.

We have time! he had claimed. *It's not that bad yet.*

I was nine. Father had never been wrong about anything before, but hearing the fear in Mother's voice, I had wondered for the first time if he could be.

The school here isn't a proper one; we've no paper and only two books that are dog-eared and faded. Sometimes we scratch our names in the dirt with sticks, but the less I write, the more I forget how to.

I had listened on the stairs when Ayah thought I was in bed.

Singapore will soon fall, she had whispered to Cook.

Japanese troops have cut off our water, Cook had replied.

Lying on our lumpy straw mattresses, adults murmur how this camp isn't the worst, but I find that hard to believe. When I can't sleep, I try to picture the paintings and chandeliers and sweeping staircase of my home. I see Father, in his uniform, smiling, as I skip downstairs to him in my party dress. His bushy moustache tickles my cheek when he hugs me. My ayah rushes after me, waving a green velvet ribbon for my hair.

On the day we finally left Mother told us that we could only bring one toy. Bobby chose a wooden train, but I thought that offered little comfort.

Here, Bobby, carry Bear if you like, I had said. I kissed one furry ear and sniffed, before handing him over.

Father had stayed behind and said he'd join us soon.

In the breakfast hut, I collect my rusty tin cup of rice and miso soup and sit next to Agnes. We share a mattress. She's two years younger than me and when she first arrived, she cried all night for months.

"I'm allowed to write a letter today," Agnes says, brightly.

I can't bear to tell her I've never received a reply from the letters I write to my aunt in England. I doubt they even reach her.

Smiling weakly at each other, we pick out the black bits from the rice.

The four of us had held hands and made our way to the port where ships waited. But my hand was wrenched from Mother's and she and Bobby were dragged further and further away. *I love you, Nell!* she had screamed, loud enough to shatter glass. Ayah gripped my hand so tightly that my fingers were bruised for a week.

When Ayah and I reached the front, the last ship had left. Then the Japanese soldiers marched forward, waving bayonets. They split us up and I never saw my ayah again.

I wince as the sticky cold rice clogs my throat. Conditions are becoming worse; some days we have no vegetables with our rice. There are more deaths from lack of food, and people get sick from worms eating them from the inside.

"There's a rumour the Germans have been defeated," Agnes mumbles.

"Really?" I immediately cover my mouth, fearing my response is too loud. My heart bangs against my ribs. Could this be true? Oh! Perhaps I will see Mother, Father and Bobby again! And Ayah! Maybe even Bear...

"Get to work!" the patrolling guard shouts.

As I walk into the hospital hut, the camp doctor shouts at me, "Help me with this wound!" He adds salt to a bowl of water and thrusts it at me.

A woman lying on a concrete slab writhes in agony. "She fell on a bamboo spike out at the work site," he grumbles. He dabs at her thigh with a cloth, ignoring her cries.

Her eyes cloud over as she gazes through me. I step to one side and gently take her hand. When this war ends, if it ever does, I'll become a doctor.

RADIO

In the 1940s, news travelled slower than it does today. There was no Internet, smartphones or 24-hour television. In fact, television broadcasts, which were very new, stopped altogether during the war years.

Instead, people relied on the radio, newsreels at cinemas and newspapers to find out what was happening. Both the Allies and Axis powers loudly celebrated their successes while other less favourable stories were played down or not mentioned at all, to keep up morale. Some news stories that might be useful to the enemy were also kept quiet.

Radio broadcasts were also used in surprising ways. BBC European radio services broadcast secret coded messages to resistance fighters. The messages, such as 'the woman stroked the dog's nose', seemed meaningless even to the radio staff, who were never told their true meaning. But they would tell agents all sorts of things, such as when documents were received, a person was safe or to cancel a mission.

Winston Churchill makes a radio address from his desk at 10 Downing Street

VE DAY

After almost six years of hardship, danger and destruction, the war came to a close in Europe when Hitler died and the Nazis surrendered.

'Victory in Europe' or 'VE Day' was declared on 8 May 1945. Miles of bunting hung from the lampposts and people put out tables and chairs for street parties.

In London, people gathered in Trafalgar Square, Piccadilly Circus and The Mall to celebrate the end of the war. But for others, the war continued and hostilities did not officially come to an end until September 1945.

VE DAY IN NUMBERS

Date of VE Day: 8 May 1945

Estimated crowd in Piccadilly Circus, London: 50,000

Second World War officially ended: 2 September 1945

Clothes rationing ended: 1949

Food rationing ended: 1954

Crowds gather in Trafalgar Square, London, on VE Day

Churchill waves to the VE Day crowds in Whitehall, London

VICTORY OVER GERMANY 1945

REMEMBRANCE AND HONOURING HEROES

The Armistice that ended the First World War was signed on 11 November 1918. It agreed that fighting would end at the 'eleventh hour of the eleventh day of the eleventh month'.

Since then, 11 November has become a day to honour those who died in all conflicts, including the Second World War.

It is usually marked with a two-minute silence at 11am to remember those who died. In Britain, parades are held on the second Sunday in November and poppy wreaths are laid at war memorials.

In the months after the First World War ended, people noticed that poppies had started to bloom across the battlefields. Since 1921, the poppy has been worn to to remember those who gave their lives in the First World War and other conflicts since.

The Cenotaph on Whitehall in London is the United Kingdom's primary war memorial

MEDALS

Military decorations are medals that are given to people who have served in the armed forces.

Some, such as the War Medal 1939–1945, were awarded to everyone who took part.

Those who showed exceptional bravery or courage were recognized with a special honour called an 'operational gallantry award', which includes the Military Cross, the Distinguished Flying Cross and the highest of all, the Victoria Cross.

The Victoria Cross may be awarded to all ranks of the services and civilians for gallantry in the presence of the enemy

TIMELINE OF
THE SECOND WORLD WAR

 1939

1 September – Hitler invades Poland. Britain evacuates children from cities.

3 September – Britain and France (the Allies) declare war on Germany.

 1940

January – rationing begins.

April – Germany invades Norway and Denmark.

May – Germany invades Belgium, France, Luxembourg and the Netherlands.
   – Winston Churchill becomes British prime minister.
   – Allied troops begin to be rescued from the beaches at Dunkirk.

June – Italy joins the war on Germany's side (the Axis powers).

July – the Battle of Britain starts.

September – The Blitz begins.

➡ 1941

June – the Axis powers invade the Soviet Union.

September – the Nazi siege of Leningrad begins. It lasts for nearly 900 days.

December – Japan attacks Pearl Harbor. The United States enters the war on the Allies' side.

➡ 1942

June – success at the Battle of Midway helps the Allies in the fight for control of the Pacific Ocean.

➡ 1943

February – Nazi defeat at Stalingrad.

September – the Allies invade Italy.

October – Italy joins the Allies.

➡ 1944

June – the Allies launch the D-Day landings in Normandy, France. The first German V-1 rocket attack on London.

August – the Resistance uprising, Paris is freed from the Nazis.

1945

April – the Soviet army advances on Berlin, Germany. Hitler dies in his bunker.

May – German troops surrender to the Allies.

8 May – Victory in Europe (VE Day).

August – the United States drops atomic bombs on Hiroshima and Nagasaki, causing destruction on a scale never seen before.

15 August – Japan surrenders – the war is over.

Vera Lynn opens variety Ladies Guild YMCA car
in London, June 1942

ABOUT THE AUTHORS

TONY BRADMAN

"Both my parents served in the Second World War. My dad was a sailor on HMS *Belfast* and my mum was also in the navy as a WREN in Portsmouth. I remember them both talking about VE Day, and how they felt when six years of war finally came to an end. I was delighted to be asked to contribute to this great anthology – it's my way of remembering them, and that day in May 1945."

Tony is the award-winning author of many children's titles, from picture books to historical fiction.

JIM ELDRIDGE

"I have a personal connection with the Second World War. I was a war baby, born in 1944 close to the heart of London's northern railway termini (Euston, Kings Cross and St Pancras), which were major targets for the Nazis – terrifyingly, the effects of a V-2 rocket explosion hit my pram and blew it over.

"Fortunately, I survived to write two stories for this anthology, to give thanks to those courageous men and women who fought against the odds, both abroad and at home, to bring liberty to this and other nations in 1945."

Jim is the award-winning author of numerous children's books. He has also written for television and radio.

··

EMILY HIBBS

"When I was little, one of my nana's favourite songs to sing was 'The White Cliffs of Dover'. Before I knew anything about the Second World War, I knew half the lyrics to that song. As I got older, she and my grampi – who had been in the RAF – told me about their experiences of the conflict. While researching this project, I discovered other hidden tales from this significant moment in history and hope that, through our stories, you will too."

Emily is an author and editor who has written on everything from unicorns to footballers.

E.L. NORRY

"When I was at school, learning about the Second World War was a topic that fascinated me and captured my imagination. Being Jewish, it was enlightening to write from the perspective of a Kindertransport child, and with *Empire of the Sun* being a favourite film, having the opportunity to imagine life in a POW camp was interesting.

"I've enjoyed taking time to imagine the lives of children who had to live through and endure such extreme and difficult times."

Emma is a rising star as a writer with a particular interest in exploring difficult issues and complex characters.

··

BALI RAI

"I was delighted to take part in this VE Day project. It remains vitally important that our children learn of the sacrifices made by all those who came before us. VE Day marked the end of a ghastly and murderous period in history. It heralded new hope for all those who experienced the Second World War. I was honoured to help commemorate that glorious moment for a new generation."

Bali has written over forty young adult, teen and children's books, and has won multiple awards.

LEILA RASHEED

"It's important to remember that wars have consequences that last for generations. We tend to think that peace is normal, but my grandfather fought in the Boer War and the First World War; my father lived through a war that changed his country from East Pakistan to Bangladesh; and the country I grew up in, Libya, recently suffered a terrible civil war.

"I hope these stories remind readers that peace should never be taken for granted."

Leila writes literature for children and teenagers, and teaches creative writing at universities.

....

GLOSSARY

Allies – the countries who fought against the Axis powers in the Second World War; the main Allied powers were Britain and the Commonwealth, France, China, the Soviet Union, Poland and the USA

Aryan – in Nazi ideas, a white-skinned (Caucasian) person not of the Jewish faith

Axis powers – Nazi Germany, Italy and Japan. Italy joined the Allies in October 1943.

ayah – a nanny or nursemaid, employed by a family to look after their children

barracks – the group of buildings that soldiers live in

bayonet – a blade attached to the end of a rifle and used for fighting

British Empire – the UK and the countries or territories it controlled

Commonwealth, the – the UK and group of states that were formerly part of the British Empire

communism – the idea that everything is owned by the community and each person in the community adds and takes according to their skills and needs

concentration camp – a place where people were imprisoned because of their beliefs or appearance and forced to work hard in inadequate conditions or executed

displaced persons camp – a place for refugees to stay until they find a new home

gallantry – brave actions during war

general election – in the UK, this is when people vote for their Members of Parliament

Geneva Conventions – the international agreements (first made in 1864) that set up the code by which sick people and prisoners of war should be treated

government-in-exile – a group that claims to be a country's government but has to operate from outside that country

Hitler, Adolf – Austrian-born leader of the German Nazi party; dictator and Chancellor of Germany 1933–1945

humanitarian – to be 'humanitarian' is to try to help others in need

Jehovah's Witness – a member of the religious movement that follows some Christian ideas; they refuse blood transfusions as well as military service, due to their religious beliefs

Jew – a member of the Jewish faith (Judaism); Judaism is based on the teachings of the Old Testament of the Bible, known as the Torah, the Talmud

Kindertransport – the movement to get children out of Nazi Europe from 1938 to 1940

Land Girl – a woman doing farm work in the Second World War

LGBT – 'lesbian, gay, bisexual and transgender'

Lord Woolton pie – a pie with vegetables, made during the war when food was rationed

merchant navy – a country's fleet of ships used for business (not military)

mess, the – the building at a barracks where soldiers go to eat

Nazi party – the National Socialist German Workers' Party led by Hitler; the Nazis were in power in Germany from 1933 to 1945

partisan – a member of an armed group fighting secretly

pogrom – organized violence against people because of their religion or race

prisoner of war (POW) – someone who has been captured by the enemy during wartime, and put in prison

Red Army – the army of the Soviet Union

Red Cross or Crescent – a humanitarian group that helps people in times of war or crisis

resistance movement – a secret group fighting against the leaders or occupiers of their country

Roma, or Romany, people – a race of people who travel from place to place

Sikh – someone who follows the religion Sikhism

Soviet Union – the Soviet Union, or USSR (Union of Soviet Socialist Republics), was the first Communist state. It united fifteen countries, the largest of which was Russia. The Soviet Union lasted from its official creation in December 1922 until its dissolution in December 1991.

SS – *Schutzstaffel*, the special police force of the Nazi party

Stalag – the German name for a prison camp housing ordinary soldiers

Star of David – a six-pointed star that is a symbol of Judaism

Sten gun – a submachine gun used by the British army in the Second World War

synagogue – a building where Jewish people go to worship or to learn

tenko – the Japanese word for 'roll call'; the register taken in Japanese POW camps

theatre of war – an area involved in war, either sea, air or ground

uprising – when a group of people fight against those who are ruling their country, to try and bring about change

welfare state – a system of free health care, education and other benefits, provided by a government

INDEX

Every effort has been made to ensure that this information is correct at the time of going to print. Any errors will be corrected upon reprint.